Volume 1

ABACUS

ARCHAEOLOGICAL TECHNIQUES

The ILLUSTRATED
SCIENCE *and*
INVENTION
ENCYCLOPEDIA

International Edition

H. S. STUTTMAN CO., INC. *publishers*   New York, N.Y. 10016

how it works

Published by H. S. STUTTMAN CO., Inc.
New York, N.Y. 10016

Introduction

THE ILLUSTRATED SCIENCE AND INVENTION ENCYCLOPEDIA is the first home reference library for the layman that concentrates on "how it works" as the medium for explaining every significant scientific discovery and every major technological breakthrough.

Every day of our lives we use dozens of machines . . . a wrist watch, a telephone, a radio, a television set, a tape recorder, a car, a bus, a train, an escalator, perhaps an electric razor . . . or a hair dryer, a cooker, a vacuum cleaner, a washing machine, a steam iron . . . the list is virtually endless.

Then there are all the things we don't come into contact with ourselves, but which have a profound influence on our lives – power stations, factories, foundries, refineries, mines, weapons, missiles, computers, communications satellites. . . .

In this fast-moving technological age, practically everyone asks himself – or is asked by a child – "how does it work?" Accurate, authentic, understandable answers will become more and more important in our lives and the lives and careers of our children. This unique new graphic introduction to the modern world of science, invention, and technology has been planned to meet this need.

THE ILLUSTRATED SCIENCE AND INVENTION ENCYCLOPEDIA is an absorbing record of man's inventive genius and his continuing quest for mastery over his environment. It reveals all the interesting, useful, fun-to-find-out details and fascinating facts about machines, tools, and devices – in fact, all the technical concepts created by the human mind and hand. It is the layman's gateway to understanding the dramatic breakthroughs in Machine Technology, Magnetics and Electronics, Light and Optics, Fluid Technology, Industrial Processes, Power Generation, Structural Engineering, Temperature Control, and other rapidly developing fields.

These unique new volumes are of immense practical value, too. The home handyman now has detailed how-it-works information that can be applied to a wide variety of do-it-yourself projects. The lavish use of full color photographs, diagrams, and exploded see-all illustrations enables the non-technical layman as well as the inventive craftsman to adapt and apply proven processes and tested technology to his own projects.

For the first time, every machine you are ever likely to hear about, or see, or actually use is clearly and simply explained – how it was discovered, who invented it, how it is made, what it is made of, and **how it works.**

Volume 1

ABACUS
A-BOMB
ABRASIVES
ACCELEROMETER
ACCORDION and concertina
ACCUMULATOR
ACETYLENE LAMP
ACHROMATIC LENS
ACID manufacture
ADHESIVES
AERIAL (antenna)
AERIAL PHOTOGRAPHY
AERO ENGINE
AEROFOIL
AEROSOL spray can
AGRICOLA, Georgius
AGRICULTURAL IMPLEMENTS
AIRBAG
AIR CONDITIONING
AIRCRAFT
AIRCRAFT history
AIR CUSHION VEHICLES
AIRLOCK
AIRPORT
AIRSHIP
AIR TRAFFIC CONTROL
ALCHEMY
ALCOHOL
ALDEHYDE
ALGAE, uses of
ALIPHATIC COMPOUNDS
ALKALI METAL
ALKALINE EARTH METAL
ALLOY
ALTERNATING CURRENT and voltage
ALTERNATOR
ALTIMETER, radar
ALUMINIUM and its compounds
ALUMINIUM extraction
ALUMINIUM welding
AMBULANCE DESIGN
AMINE
AMINO ACIDS
AMMETER
AMMONIA
AMMUNITION

AMPERE
AMPHIBIOUS VEHICLES
AMPLIFIER
AM RADIO
ANAESTHETIC MACHINES
ANALYSIS, chemical
ANCHOR
ANEMOMETER
ANTI-AIRCRAFT GUN
ANTIBIOTIC MANUFACTURE
ANTI-FOULING TECHNIQUES
AQUALUNG
ARCHAELOGICAL
   TECHNIQUES

Volume 2

ARCHES
ARCHIMEDEAN SCREW
ARCHIMEDES
ARC LAMP
ARMOUR
ARMOUR PIERCING SHELL
AROMATIC COMPOUNDS
ARRESTING MECHANISM
ARTIFICIAL BONES
   AND JOINTS
ARTIFICIAL LIMBS, history
ARTIFICIAL LIMBS, modern
ASBESTOS
ASDIC and sonar
ASPIRIN MANUFACTURE
ASSEMBLY LINE
ASTROCOMPASS
ASTROLABE
ASTRONOMICAL TELESCOPE
ASTROPHYSICS
ATMOSPHERIC ENGINE
ATMOSPHERIC RAILWAY
ATOM and its mechanism
ATOMIC CLOCK
ATOMIZER
AUDIO-VISUAL AID equipment
AUTOCLAVE
AUTOGYRO
AUTOMATIC CONTROL
AUTOMATIC PISTOL
AUTOMATIC TRANSMISSION

AVIONICS
AVOGADRO, Amedeo
BABBAGE, Charles
BACK-PEDAL BRAKE
BACON, Roger
BACON CURING
BAGGAGE HANDLING systems
BAILEY BRIDGE
BAIRD, John Logie
BALANCES
BALLISTA
BALLOON
BALLPOINT PEN
BANKNOTE ACCEPTING
   MACHINE
BARBED WIRE manufacture
BAROMETERS
BARREL ORGAN
BASKET MAKING
BATHYSCAPHE
BATTERY, electric
BATTERY and intensive farming
BAZOOKA and other small rockets
BEARINGS
BECQUEREL, Henri
BEER AND BREWING
BELL, Alexander Graham

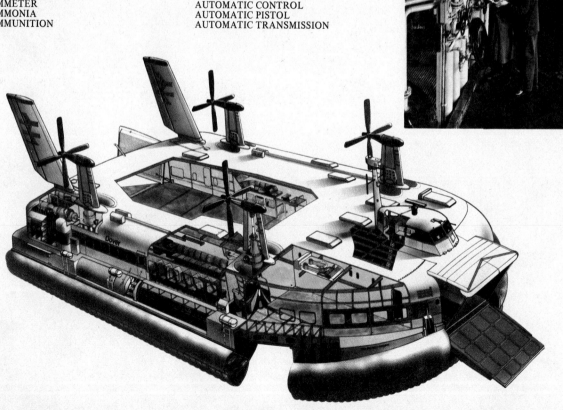

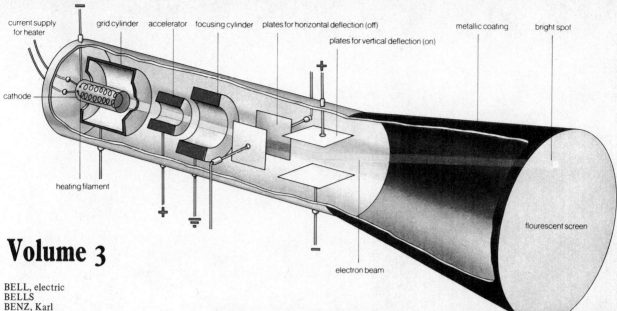

current supply for heater
grid cylinder
accelerator
focusing cylinder
plates for horizontal deflection (off)
plates for vertical deflection (on)
metallic coating
bright spot
cathode
heating filament
flourescent screen
electron beam

Volume 3

Volume 4

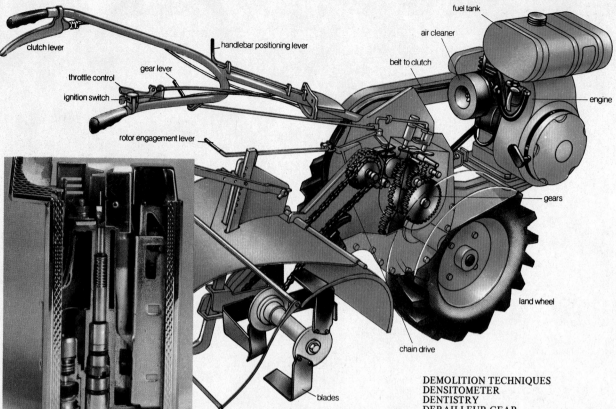

clutch lever

handlebar positioning lever

fuel tank

air cleaner

belt to clutch

gear lever

throttle control

ignition switch

engine

rotor engagement lever

gears

land wheel

chain drive

blades

Volume 7

Volume 8

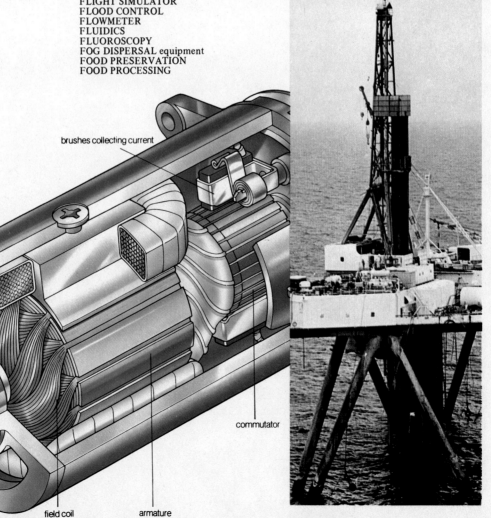

brushes collecting current

ball bearing

commutator

ventilation slot

field coil

armature

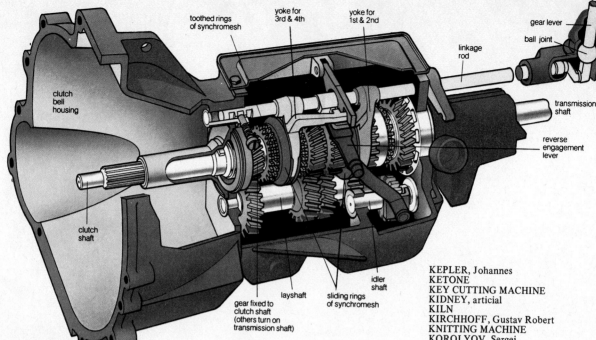

clutch bell housing

clutch shaft

toothed rings of synchromesh

yoke for 3rd & 4th

yoke for 1st & 2nd

linkage rod

gear lever

ball joint

transmission shaft

reverse engagement lever

gear fixed to clutch shaft (others turn on transmission shaft)

layshaft

sliding rings of synchromesh

idler shaft

Volume 9

Volume 10

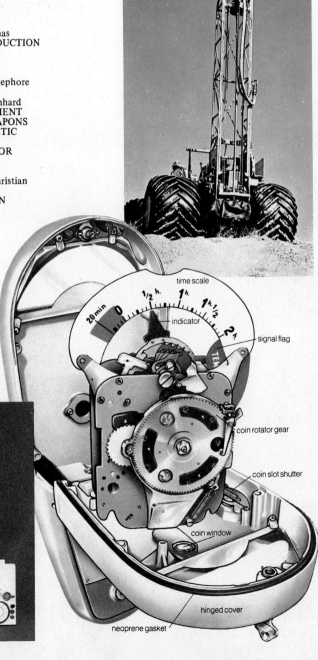

time scale
20 min 1/2 h. 1 h. 1 h. 1/2 2 h.
indicator
signal flag
coin rotator gear
coin slot shutter
coin window
hinged cover
neoprene gasket

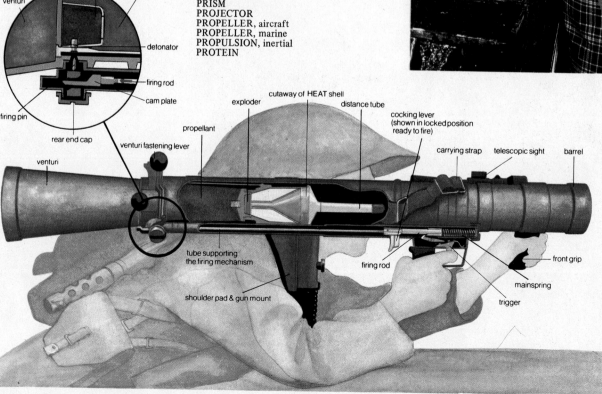

plastic blow-out disc
priming charge
venturi
propellant
detonator
firing rod
cam plate
firing pin
rear end cap
venturi

venturi fastening lever
propellant
exploder
cutaway of HEAT shell
distance tube
cocking lever
(shown in locked position
ready to fire)
carrying strap
telescopic sight
barrel
tube supporting
the firing mechanism
firing rod
front grip
mainspring
trigger
shoulder pad & gun mount

Volume 15

Volume 16

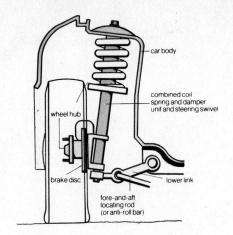

car body
combined coil
spring and damper
unit and steering swivel
wheel hub
brake disc
lower link
fore-and-aft
locating rod
(or anti-roll bar)

Volume 17

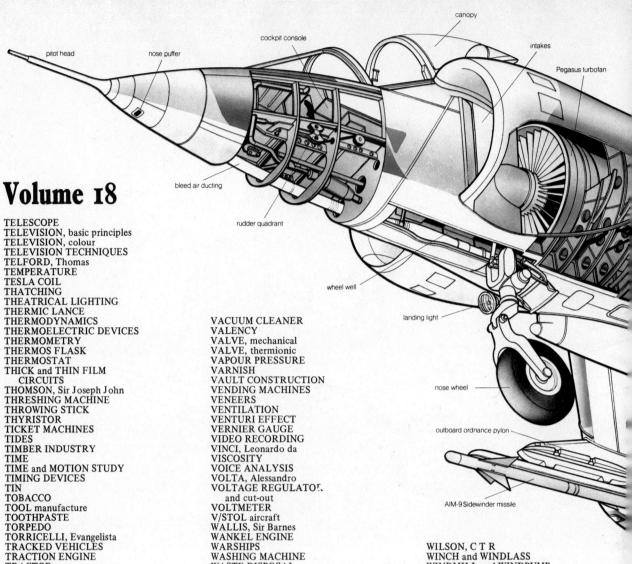

pitot head · nose puffer · cockpit console · canopy · intakes · Pegasus turbofan · bleed air ducting · rudder quadrant · wheel well · landing light · nose wheel · outboard ordnance pylon · AIM-9 Sidewinder missile

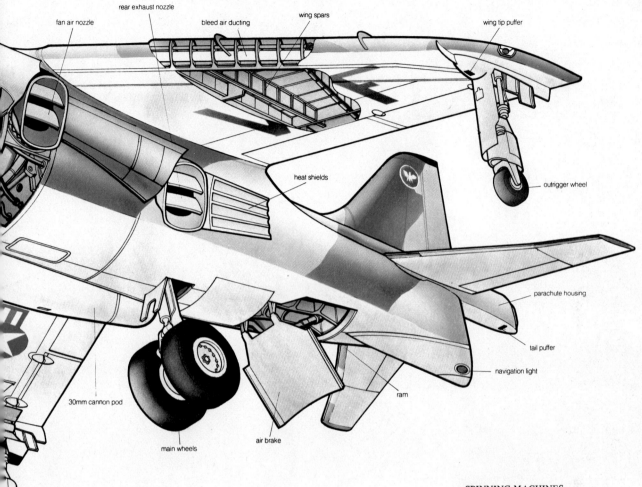

fan air nozzle

rear exhaust nozzle

bleed air ducting

wing spars

wing tip puffer

heat shields

outrigger wheel

parachute housing

tail puffer

navigation light

ram

30mm cannon pod

main wheels

air brake

Volume 21

HISTORIC INVENTIONS

ABACUS

The abacus is a hand-operated calculating machine in which numbers are represented by beads strung on rods or wires set in a rectangular frame. It is an extremely ancient device that has been in use for thousands of years in various forms, and is still commonly used in China, Japan and parts of the Middle East. The original version was probably a tray of sand divided into strips by pieces of wood. Marks were made in the sand and wiped out again as required.

The most usual form of abacus is the Chinese *suan pan* ('reckoning board'). This has up to 13 columns of beads, each divided in two by a crossbar running right across the frame. In each column there are two beads above the crossbar and five below it. Some other types have one and four beads respectively, but these are less easy to use.

In the far right-hand column, each lower bead represents one, and each upper bead five. This is the 'units' column. The one to the left of it is the 'tens' column, and here each lower bead represents 10 and each upper bead 50. The next column is the 'hundreds' column, where each lower bead represents 100 and each upper bead 500. This continues leftwards with thousands, tens of thousands and so on. A 13-column abacus can register numbers up to 9,999,999,999,999.

Numbers are 'entered' on the abacus by moving beads to touch the crossbar. To enter the number 23, for example, three lower beads are slid up the 'units' column to the bar, and two are slid up the 'tens' column.

To add 6 to this, one *upper* bead is slid *down* the 'units' column to the bar (thus adding 5) and one lower bead is slid up to the bar (adding another 1, making 6 in all). The abacus now reads 29.

If another 1 is added by sliding the last lower 'unit' bead up to the bar, there will be no more lower beads against the outside of the frame in this column. The lower part of the column is considered as 'full' and must be 'cancelled' immediately. This is done by sliding all five beads back to the outside of the frame and moving down one upper bead (worth 5) to take their place.

In this case, there is already one upper bead against the bar, so moving the other one down 'fills' the upper part of the units column too. This is also cancelled and one more lower bead moved up the next column, which is the 'tens' column, to add ten to the total. There are now no beads entered in the 'units' column, and three in the lower part of the 'tens' column. The abacus therefore reads 30, the correct answer.

Of course, a skilled operator would foresee, and so miss out, most of the intermediate steps in the procedure. With practice, it is possible to calculate at very high speed on an abacus — at least as fast as an ordinary electric adding machine.

Subtraction is performed by exactly the opposite process:

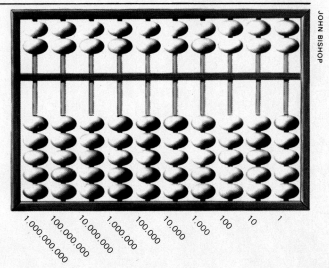

1,000,000,000   100,000,000   10,000,000   1,000,000   100,000   10,000   1,000   100   10   1

Beads in the upper section have five times the value of the lower ones.

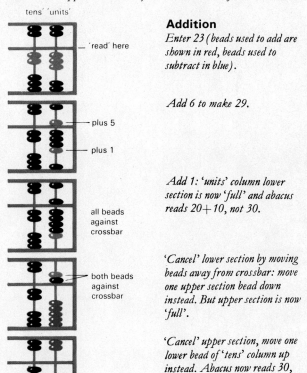

tens' 'units'

— 'read' here

— plus 5

— plus 1

all beads against crossbar

both beads against crossbar

Addition

Enter 23 (beads used to add are shown in red, beads used to subtract in blue).

Add 6 to make 29.

Add 1: 'units' column lower section is now 'full' and abacus reads 20+10, not 30.

'Cancel' lower section by moving beads away from crossbar: move one upper section bead down instead. But upper section is now 'full'.

'Cancel' upper section, move one lower bead of 'tens' column up instead. Abacus now reads 30, the right result.

for example, three is subtracted by moving three beads away from the crossbar in the lower part of the column.

The abacus is basically an adding and subtracting machine, and cannot be used to multiply by any one-stage process. This was a source of difficulty to the ancient Chinese — and the Romans, who used a comparable type of abacus. Neither the Roman nor the traditional Chinese numeral system allowed them to write numbers in columns, so they could not write down multiplication sums in the way used today.

For multiplication by a number up to, say, five, the number to be multiplied can just be added to itself the right number of times. But with larger numbers, this would take an inconvenient length of time, so another method must be used.

The two numbers (say 478 and 35) are written side by side, on a separate piece of paper, and under whichever of them is more convenient, half of that number is written. If this is not a whole number ($35 \div 2 = 17\frac{1}{2}$) the fraction is discounted (17). The half is now halved and halved again by the same method, right down to one: 35; 17; 8; 4; 2; 1. The other number is now doubled and re-doubled in a similar way, the same number of times as the first number was halved — this is a very quick series of additions on the abacus.

The sum now looks like this:

$$
\begin{array}{rr}
478 & \times \ 35 \\
956 & 17 \\
1912 & 8 \\
3824 & 4 \\
7648 & 2 \\
15296 & 1 \\
\end{array}
$$

The next stage is to strike out all the lines where the *halved* number is *even* (this would include the top line if it were even), leaving those where the halved number is odd:

$$
\begin{array}{rr}
478 & \times \ 35 \\
956 & 17 \\
15296 & 1 \\
\end{array}
$$

The doubled column is now added up on the abacus: $478 + 956 + 15296 = 16730$, which is the right answer.

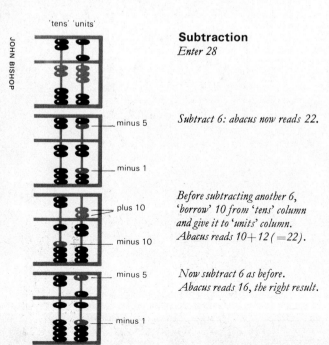

'tens' 'units'

JOHN BISHOP

minus 5

minus 1

plus 10

minus 10

minus 5

minus 1

Subtraction
Enter 28

Subtract 6: abacus now reads 22.

Before subtracting another 6, 'borrow' 10 from 'tens' column and give it to 'units' column. Abacus reads $10 + 12 (= 22)$.

Now subtract 6 as before. Abacus reads 16, the right result.

A-BOMB

The A-bomb, or atomic bomb, has been used only twice in war, at Hiroshima and Nagasaki, but both times it has totally destroyed a large city in a single explosion. Although it has now been supplanted by the even more powerful H-BOMB, or hydrogen bomb, it is still a weapon of appalling power, and one that has significantly changed the history of the world.

Strictly speaking, the term 'atomic bomb' includes the H-bomb, which also uses atomic power. But in general usage, 'atomic bomb' is reserved for earlier weapons that work by nuclear FISSION, that is, splitting atoms. The hydrogen bomb works by nuclear FUSION — joining small atoms together to make larger ones. Both fission and fusion release huge amounts of energy, causing an explosion.

Today, A-bombs are considered by the major world powers as obsolete weapons. But they are still needed as 'triggers' to set off hydrogen bombs, and have also been used to replace conventional chemical explosives for certain kinds of civil engineering projects. In Russia, for example, silver is mined in this way. There are also plans to use the technique for digging canals.

Nuclear fission The huge power of an atomic bomb comes from the forces holding each individual ATOM of a substance together. These forces are akin to, though not actually the same as, magnetism. Every atom of every substance that exists is held together by them. The energy released by splitting one atom is tiny, but there are so many billion atoms in even the smallest piece of material that a great deal of power is released by breaking up all its atoms.

Most naturally occurring elements (pure substances) have very stable atoms which are impossible to split except by using such techniques as bombarding them in a particle ACCELERATOR. But there is one natural element whose atoms can be split comparatively easily; this is the metal uranium. Its special property comes from the very large size of its atoms; they are too big to hold together firmly.

Atoms are (for practical purposes) made up of three kinds of sub-atomic particles, tiny fragments of matter which are the same in all atoms of all elements. These are protons and neutrons which cluster together to form the nucleus or central mass, of the atom, and elecotrns, which spin round the nucleus like planets around the sun. The lighter the element, the smaller the number of sub-atomic particles in its atoms.

Uranium is an extremely heavy metal, heavier than gold, and it has the largest atoms of any natural element. Moreover, they have far more neutrons than protons, which does not make them easier to split, but does have an important bearing on their ability to cause an explosion.

There are two ISOTOPES of uranium: an isotope is a form of an element distinguished by the number of neutrons in its atom. Natural uranium consists mostly of the isotope U-238, which has 92 protons and 146 neutrons ($92 + 146 = 238$). But mixed in with this is about 0.6 per cent of the other isotope, U-235, which has the same number of protons but only 143 neutrons. This isotope, unlike U-238, is fissionable (its atoms can be split), and so it is the one used for making bombs.

Both isotopes of uranium, and certain other heavy elements, are naturally radioactive, that is, their big, unstable atoms slowly disintegrate in the course of time. The 'spare' neutrons are thrown off, and so are various other particles. Left to themselves, uranium atoms eventually lose so many particles that they turn into a completely different element, the metal lead. This change, however, takes many thousand years before

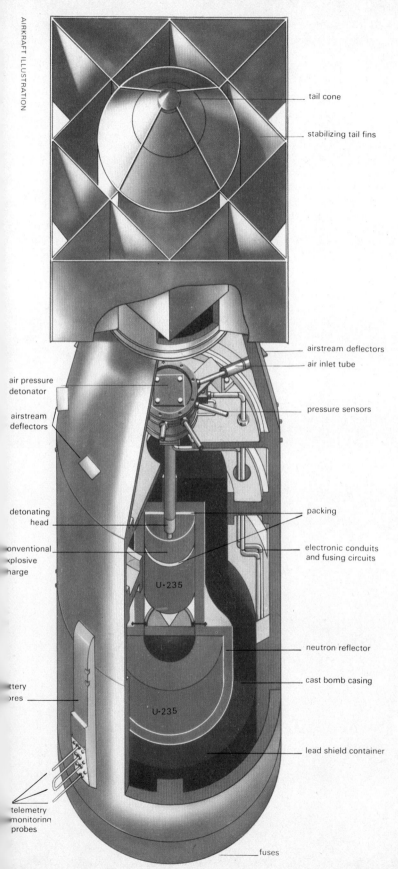

tail cone

stabilizing tail fins

airstream deflectors

air inlet tube

air pressure detonator

airstream deflectors

pressure sensors

detonating head

conventional explosive charge

packing

electronic conduits and fusing circuits

U-235

U-235

neutron reflector

cast bomb casing

battery cores

lead shield container

telemetry monitoring probes

fuses

Left: a cutaway view of the U-235 bomb 'Little Boy'.
Below: the chain reaction that fuelled it. To start the
reaction, only one neutron need strike one U-235 atom.
This turns it into U-236, an unstable form that
immediately disintegrates, releasing more neutrons to
strike other atoms and split them.
Second from bottom) the bomb fell right on the centre
of Hiroshima. This map shows the extent of the
damage.
Bottom) a plutonium bomb of the 'Fat Man' type,
such as was dropped on Nagasaki.

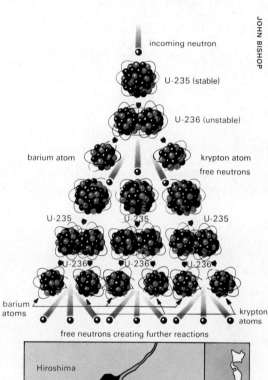

incoming neutron

U-235 (stable)

U-236 (unstable)

barium atom

krypton atom
free neutrons

U-235   U-235   U-235

U-236   U-236   U-236

barium atoms

krypton atoms

free neutrons creating further reactions

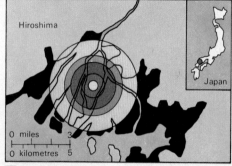

Hiroshima

Japan

0 miles   3
0 kilometres   5

□ everything vaporized
■ total destruction
■ severe blast damage
■ everything flammable burnt
□ serious fires

a measurable number of atoms have turned to lead.

Atoms of U-235 can be made to break up much faster than this in a chain reaction. Instead of disintegrating slowly by themselves, the atoms are forcibly split by neutrons forcing their way into the nucleus. A U-235 atom is so unstable that a blow from a single neutron is enough to split it. Usually it splits into two smaller atoms of different elements, such as barium and krypton.

When a U-235 atom splits, it gives off energy in the form of heat and gamma radiation, the most powerful form of radioactivity and the one which is most harmful to life. It also gives off two or three of its 'spare' neutrons, which are not needed to make the barium and krypton atoms. These fly out with sufficient force to split other atoms if they hit them.

In theory, it is necessary only to split one U-235 atom, and the neutrons from this will split other atoms, which in turn will split more, and so on. This is why the reaction is called a 'chain' reaction. It happens with great speed; all the atoms split within a millionth of a second.

In practice, it is not quite so simple to start a nuclear explosion. There has to be a certain weight of U-235 present before the chain reaction will sustain itself. If there is less than this amount there will be too few atoms to ensure that neutrons from every atom that splits will hit other atoms.

The minimum amount is known as the critical mass. The actual mass depends on the purity of the material, but for pure U-235, it is 110 lb (50 kg). No U-235 ever is quite pure, so in reality more is needed.

Uranium is not the only material used for making A-bombs. Another material is the element plutonium, in its isotope Pu-239. Plutonium is not found naturally (except in minute traces) and is always made from uranium. This can be done by putting U-238 in a NUCLEAR REACTOR. After a while, the intense radioactivity causes it to pick up extra particles, so that more and more of its atoms turn into plutonium.

Plutonium will not start a fast chain reaction by itself, but this difficulty is overcome by having a neutron source, a highly radioactive material that gives off neutrons faster than the plutonium itself. In certain types of bomb, a mixture of the elements beryllium and polonium is used. Only a small piece is needed; the material is not fissionable in itself, but is just there to act as a 'starter'.

Mechanism of the bomb

There is more to an A-bomb than just the nuclear fuel. Fairly elaborate equipment is needed to set it off, and there are also safety devices to make it absolutely impossible to set off by accident.

A bomb cannot be made simply by putting a piece of uranium larger than critical mass into a casing, because this would cause it to go off immediately. Instead, two or more pieces are inserted a safe distance apart and 'assembled', or shot together, to start a chain reaction.

The simplest possible atomic bomb is one of the type dropped on Hiroshima. It is known as a 'gun-type' bomb, and actually does contain a gun. At one end of the barrel there is a 'target', a piece of U-235 slightly smaller than critical mass and shaped like a sphere with a conical wedge removed from it. This gap in the sphere reaches right down to its centre and faces towards the other end of the barrel.

At the other end of the barrel there is another, smaller, piece of U-235 in the shape of a cone with its point towards the gap in the target. It is the exact shape of the piece missing from the sphere. Together, the two pieces are just over critical mass.

The smaller piece is backed by a charge of ordinary high explosive. When this is set off, the cone is shot into the sphere and the force of the impact welds the two pieces together solidly. The explosion follows instantly.

Plutonium bombs are slightly more sophisticated. Plutonium is even more easily fissionable than U-235, and its critical mass is lower: 35.2 lb (16 kg) for pure Pu-239.

The mass can be reduced further, to 22 lb or 10 kg, by making a sphere of this weight of plutonium and surrounding it with non-fissionable U-238, which 'reflects' neutrons back into the centre of the sphere and minimizes loss to the outside.

Plutonium cannot be exploded so easily by a gun-type device. It has to be 'assembled' with much greater speed than uranium or it will not explode properly.

Plutonium is therefore assembled by a technique known as implosion. A number of wedge-shaped pieces of plutonium, which together will build up into a sphere, are arranged at equal intervals around a neutron source. Explosive charges of exactly equal weight are placed behind each wedge and all are detonated together. The wedges shoot towards the centre and touch each other at the same moment. This technique was used for the second American atomic bomb, which was dropped on Nagasaki.

Apart from the basic mechanism that starts the chain reaction there has to be some device for setting off the explosive. This depends on the exact nature and use of the bomb. The

This United States A-bomb test was carried out at Bikini Atoll in the Pacific on 25 July 1946. The picture was taken fractions of a second after the blast, before the 'mushroom' cloud had time to form. Note the circular shock wave on the water and the captured German warships being exposed to the effects of the blast (lower left).

US ATOMIC ENERGY COMMISSION

Hiroshima and Nagasaki bombs were both worked by built-in ALTIMETERS, so that they exploded automatically when they had fallen to a certain height above the city. This ensured the maximum amount of destruction.

Development of the bomb
If U-235 had been obtainable by simply refining uranium ore, the first atomic bomb would have been built years before the Second World War. But U-235 is very hard to extract. Every 25,000 tons of uranium ore yields about 50 tons of pure uranium metal, but 99.3% of this metal is U-238. Furthermore, no ordinary chemical extraction process can separate the two isotopes, since they have precisely similar chemical characteristics. Anything that is done to the U-235 to purify it has exactly the same effect on the U-238.

The only methods that will work in separating the isotopes are strictly mechanical ones. All work on the principle that individual atoms of U-235 are slightly, but only slightly, lighter than those of U-238.

On August 2nd 1939, just before the beginning of World War II, the scientist Albert Einstein wrote to the then President of the United States, Franklin D. Roosevelt. In his letter, he pointed out that the Germans were already trying to purify U-235 and build a bomb.

Accordingly, the United States Government set up the giant Manhattan Project, an undertaking committed to producing a workable bomb with the utmost speed.

The first and main problem was to find how to produce enough 'enriched' uranium, that is, with more U-235 than usual, to sustain a chain reaction. The enrichment methods they devised are still used today.

The American scientists designed and built a gigantic enrichment plant at Oak Ridge, Tennessee. The plant worked on the principle of gaseous diffusion, a system devised by H. C. Urey and his associates in 1940 at Columbia University.

In this system, uranium is combined with fluorine to form uranium hexafluoride gas. Next, impelled by pumps, the gas is forced through a long series of extremely fine porous barriers. Because the U-235 atoms are lighter and faster than U-238, they can penetrate the barriers more quickly, with the result that their concentration becomes slightly greater as they pass through each barrier. After passing several thousand barriers, the uranium hexafluoride contains a relatively high percentage of U-235 — 2% in the case of reactor fuel, and considerably more in the case of fissionable material for atomic bombs. Theoretically, the concentration could be as great as 95 per cent U-235.

Gaseous diffusion produces most of the enriched uranium in the world today. But the highly enriched metal for the first A-bombs, consisting of 85% U-235, was more thoroughly purified by magnetic separation. Here, uranium tetrachloride gas is electrically charged and directed past a strong magnet. Since the lightweight U-235 particles in the gas stream are less affected by the magnet, they can be separated gradually from the flow. This system was devised under Ernest O. Lawrence, the inventor of the cyclotron, at the University of California, Berkeley.

The site of the city of Nagasaki two months after it was bombed. The buildings still standing in the foreground and background mark the edges of the area of total destruction. The flat area between them is the city centre, now razed completely to the ground. No new grass has grown, since it has been killed by the radiation.

A third enrichment process, using a gas CENTRIFUGE, is becoming widespread. In this system, centrifugal force is used to separate the isotopes of uranium by their mass.

Plutonium, the second fissionable fuel, is found naturally in pitchblende and fergusonite ores, but in minute quantities: about seven parts in a million million parts of pitchblende concentrate, for instance. In practice, plutonium is easily manufactured in nuclear reactors. The plutonium for the Nagasaki bomb was produced in three reactors built under strict secrecy at Hanford, Washington, and completed in 1943.

The struggle to make enough fissionable material in time turned into a race between the uranium and plutonium producers. As it turned out, the plutonium was ready first, and a trial bomb was tested on July 16th 1945 at Trinity Site, a patch of desert near Alamogordo, New Mexico.

Three weeks later, the first uranium bomb was dropped on Hiroshima. It was a gun-type bomb nicknamed 'Little Boy' to distinguished it from the bulkier plutonium bomb, 'Fat Man'.

Sixty-six thousand people were killed and 69,000 injured at Hiroshima. When a second bomb was detonated over Nagasaki three days later, 39,000 more were killed and 25,000 injured.

ABRASIVES

Abrasives are hard substances used for rubbing off material from softer workpieces. The abrasive effect is produced almost entirely by the simple physical process of the harder substance shearing or fracturing small chips off the workpiece. In metals, the chipped-off fragments are oxidised by the air so that they do not weld themselves back on.

Abrasives are used in three main ways. One is to use the abrasive material directly on a substance: sharpening a knife on a grinding wheel is an example of this. Another is to coat another substance, such as a piece of paper, cloth or rubber of a metal disc, with granules of abrasive material, and use this as a tool: sandpaper is the commonest application of this technique. The third method is sandblasting or gritblasting, where a powerful stream of air containing abrasive particles is directed at an object to abrade its surface.

Apart from their use in sharpening-stones and grinding wheels, direct-action abrasives are also used in powder form. Most domestic cleaning agents (except soap and washing powder) contain abrasives, which are generally silica, pumice or aluminium oxide ground to a very fine powder. The chemical action of the cleaning agent is helped by the abrasive, and the two substances clean faster than either would alone.

Toothpaste also contains a mild abrasive, which is generally finely powdered chalk. Old-fashioned tooth powder often contained powdered pumice or silica, which wore the enamel off the teeth in a short time, but manufacturers now claim that the cleaning action of their product is mostly chemical

Most abrasives used in industry are applied indirectly by being stuck to a backing. This saves expense because less abrasive is used than in a solid block.

The simplest type of coated abrasive material is sandpaper, which is made by simply glueing granules of abrasive material to a sheet of paper.

Abrasive papers are made in a vast range of types, and have many uses. One unusual application is in the printing industry, where a sheet that is to be printed on both sides is laid on a sheet of abrasive paper called tympan (abrasive side up) while the second side is printed. In this way, the already printed side can rest on the abrasive points, which hold it steady and

prevent the wet ink from smearing.

Abrasive-coated belts are used in many industrial sanding machines. These may be made of extra strong paper, or else a fine, strong cloth such as linen or gaberdine is used.

Gritblasting with a machine is a versatile technique. It has the important feature that the workpiece is abraded more or less evenly all over the surface that faces the blast. It is used for cleaning metal objects thoroughly before they are electro-plated — the plating will not stick to dirt or corrosion. It is also used for incising patterns on plate glass. The area of the glass that is to be left smooth is protected with a tough paper stencil that is only partly eaten away by the blasting. This technique has replaced the older one of etching patterns on glass with hydrofluoric acid.

Types of abrasive material   Abrasive materials may be either natural or synthetic. Traditional abrasives are all natural, and the synthetic ones are a fairly recent innovation.

The oldest abrasive of all is sand, which was used for

LONDON STONE

Far left: cutting discs are coated with minute particles of industrial diamond. Abrasive discs of this type are used to cut very hard materials which would blunt an ordinary metal saw in seconds. Here, they are cutting up a block of synthetic quartz for use in quartz crystal oscillators. Water is being sprayed on to the cut to reduce the heat caused by friction.

Left: gritblasting is a technique often used to clean buildings. This picture shows a workman cleaning the London Law Courts, where the thickness of dirt ranges from ⅛ in. to an incredible 2 in. (3-50 mm). The grit is made from quarried rock, which is crushed and sieved to give the necessary fineness. Compressed air at a pressure of 40 to 60 pounds per square inch (2.8-4.2 kg/cm²) is used to blow the grit through the nozzle of the hose held by the workman. The machine uses an average of two tons of grit a day. This can be recovered from the ground at the foot of the building, but it is generally discarded. Thousands of tons are used in cleaning a building of this size, but the grit would have to be washed before it could be re-used — an expensive business.

Other uses for gritblasting include the cleaning of metal before it is electroplated. The grit also roughens the surface, giving the plating a firm hold.

polishing stone weapons as early as 25,000 BC.

Other abrasive materials in use from early times include garnet (a hard, glasslike gemstone), emery, pumice, and silica (silicon dioxide) which occurs in various forms as quartz, flint and agate. In the Middle Ages, grinding wheels of quartz and flint fragments naturally bonded together in rock were used. Gemstones were 'lapped' or polished by the use of emery or sandstone powder rubbed on with metal plates.

Sandpaper was discovered slightly later, and was followed by emery paper and cloth, which are finer grained and longer lasting, and corundum, discovered in 1825.

The most important step in the development of synthetic abrasives was made in 1891, when Edward Acheson first produced crystals of silicon carbide. This material was called Carborundum, and has been one of the most versatile synthetic abrasives. The crystals, which can be made in any required degree of fineness, can be bonded together in a solid block or used for coating metal discs or belts for use in machine tools.

Other, more recent developments include aluminium oxide, a synthetic form of corundum, and synthetic diamonds, first produced in 1955. These have not ousted natural diamonds, however, which are still better for bonding on to the steel discs which are used for cutting stone and concrete. Synthetic diamonds are used mainly for cutting and shaping other very hard substances, such as tungsten carbide. They are produced from carbon at high temperature and pressure, as are natural ones.

Diamond, the hardest natural substance, was already in use as an abrasive in India in 700 BC. Solid pieces of diamond were used for metal cutting and incising. But its rarity and cost restricted its use.

ABSOLUTE TEMPERATURE (see temperature)

ABSOLUTE ZERO (see temperature)

ABSORPTION (see sorption)

ACCELERATION (see kinematics)

ACCELEROMETER

An accelerometer is an instrument for measuring acceleration. There are two types, which are used for measuring linear (straight-line) and angular (twisting) accelerations.

Accelerometers may also be used to measure deceleration, such as the braking force of a car. They are much used in the motor industry both to measure the forward acceleration and deceleration of a car, and to measure the sideways and up-and-down accelerations caused by cornering and bumpy roads.

Other uses include testing the strength of safety belts (by measuring the deceleration force at which they break when carrying a known load) and to study vibrations in the hulls of ships and the wingtips of aircraft.

The linear accelerometer usually contains a body of known mass attached to a coil spring and free to move only along the axis of the spring, i.e. a straight line down the middle of the coil. This line is called the sensitive axis of the accelerometer, and in measuring the acceleration of any moving object, the axis must be placed in line with the direction of movement.

The tension of the spring and the weight of the body on its end are adjusted so that when a known force is applied to the accelerometer along the sensitive axis, the body moves a known distance along the spring. The body is connected to a dial, which registers its displacement.

The dial is calibrated by placing the accelerometer on a body of known acceleration and marking the position of the indicator. If this is repeated with various known accelerations, the marks will provide enough information to allow the rest of the scale to be filled in.

Linear acceleration can be measured in various units. Moderate forces are generally measured in units such as feet per second per second, also written ft/s^2, which is the number of feet per second a body adds to its speed every second. Higher forces are generally measured in 'g' units, i.e. how many times greater they are than the force of gravity. One g, the acceleration of an object falling normally to the ground, is $32\ ft/s^2$.

The angular accelerometer works on a similar principle, but is shaped differently so as to measure circular acceleration, such as might be given to the flywheel of an engine. The body of known mass is a disc pivoted on a spiral spring. The acceleration makes the disc revolve, twisting the spring. Angular acceleration is also measurable in ft/s^2 (or its metric equivalent) but the distance of the object from the centre around which it revolves must be stated as well.

Above: this dummy, used by the MIRA road safety laboratory in Nuneaton, Warwickshire for car accident research, has an accelerometer in its head, more in its torso and abdomen (silver boxes on the folding 'doors') and others in its legs (not shown).

Right: a 'Tapley' brake testing meter, a simple linear accelerometer. It is set on a heavy iron base to hold it steady. Braking swings the magnetized pendulum, moving with it a light armature geared to a dial. The dial is held in position until it is reset for the next test.

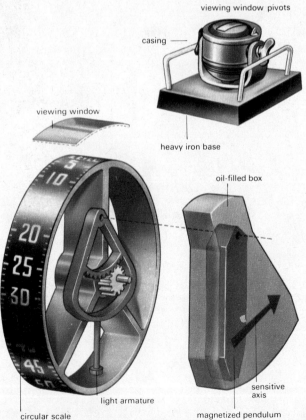

viewing window pivots

casing

viewing window

heavy iron base

oil-filled box

sensitive axis

light armature

circular scale

magnetized pendulum

ACCORDION and concertina

The accordion and concertina are closely similar instruments which are also related to the HARMONICA and HARMONIUM. All are multiple-reed instruments, in which air is blown through a gap across a metal strip (the reed) which vibrates to produce a note. The pitch is determined by the length of the reed, which is played by pressing a key.

In both instruments, air is supplied by alternately squeezing and pulling a bellows. This creates a draught in alternate directions, but the reeds will only work in one direction. Accordingly, there have to be two reeds for each note, one facing in each direction. Each has a one-way valve mounted in front of it so that air cannot be blown through backwards.

The reeds are generally made of spring steel mounted in an aluminium reed plate (brass was used in older instruments). There may be between five and over 300 reeds—accordions often have several 'registers' to produce different tones.

On some simpler instruments there is only one reed for each note, so that squeezing and pulling the bellows while a particular reed is depressed produces two different notes. This halves the number of reeds needed, but restricts the number of playable tunes.

The bellows is made from strips of cardboard covered with linen to form the hinge of each section. The corners, which are most prone to wear, are reinforced with leather and metal.

The difference between the two types is that the concertina is a small, simple instrument, octagonal in cross section, while the accordion is larger, has more notes, and is rectangular in section. In the concertina, the keys are in the form of small buttons worked by both hands. The accordion has a piano keyboard for the player's right hand, with which the main melody is played, and a set of buttons for the left hand. These act on several reeds at once to produce chords, which are used to support the melody.

The accordion was invented in the early years of the nineteenth century, but it is not certain who invented it. The original type, the 'diatone' accordion, was a small, primitive instrument without double-acting reeds. Sir Charles Wheatstone, the famous scientist and inventor of the WHEATSTONE BRIDGE and STEREOSCOPE, improved the original design in 1829 to produce the concertina. This had double reeds from the start. Modern piano accordions, however, of which there are several types, are far more complex and considerably larger than concertinas.

Above : the keyboard of the treble side of a piano accordion, showing the mechanism that opens the valves and admits air to the reeds. Each key is pivoted at the far end and attached to a metal arm. Pressing the key moves the arm outwards with the valve cover (black).

Right : a concertina opened out to display the working parts. At the top, the soundboard with reeds (shiny metal) and leather one-way valve flaps (black). Below, the button and wire mechanism that opens and closes the reeds at the other end.

ACCUMULATOR

An accumulator is a device for storing electricity. It resembles an ordinary BATTERY in many ways and, like a battery, it produces electricity by means of a chemical reaction. But the reaction is reversible, so that when the battery has discharged all its power it can be recharged by passing an electric current through it. This process can be repeated time and time again.

There are various types of accumulator in use today but the vast majority are of the *lead-acid* type. Car 'batteries' are in fact lead-acid accumulators. In its simplest form, a lead-acid accumulator consists of two *plates,* one of lead and one of lead dioxide, immersed in a weak solution of sulphuric acid known as the *electrolyte*. There are contacts on top of the plates so that electric current can be drawn from them.

A chemical reaction produces an electric current because the ATOMS of which chemical elements (pure substances) are made are held together by electrical forces when they react to form compounds.

The outer layer of an atom is composed of *electrons,* tiny particles each carrying a negative electrical charge. These particles are not all permanently attached to their atoms, and are exchanged between them during chemical reactions.

When an atom gains an electron, it gains an extra negative charge, and so becomes negatively charged as a whole. When it loses one, on the other hand, it becomes positively charged. Atoms or groups of atoms in this charged state are known as *ions*. Positive and negative ions are attracted to each other, and when circumstances allow, will move together and combine to form compounds. Ions with similar charges repel each other.

The electrons of the atoms of a metal are very easily detached. An electric current consists of a flow of electrons through a metal, hopping from atom to atom (this is why metals conduct electricity better than other substances).

Some substances are strongly *reactive,* that is, they have a strong tendency to form compounds. Sulphuric acid is one of these, which accounts for its corrosiveness.

The chemical formula of sulphuric acid is H_2SO_4: each molecule contains two atoms of hydrogen (H), one of sulphur (S) and four of oxygen (O). The hydrogen ions carry positive charges (this is shown for convenience by the symbol H^+); the sulphur and oxygen atoms are locked together to form a sulphate ion, SO_4^{--}.

The acid's reactiveness is due to the fact that the hydrogen ions are not at all firmly bonded to the rest of the molecules, so that the basic H_2SO_4 molecule breaks up readily into separate ions, either $H^+ + HSO_4^-$ or $H^+ + H^+ + SO_4^=$ (written $2H^+ + SO_4^{--}$ for short, the double positive charge being taken for granted). Substances with molecules in this state are said to be *partly dissociated*.

As long as there are no external forces at work, the dissociated ions of the acid do not react either with the pure lead negative plate or with the lead dioxide positive plate. There is a certain amount of chemical activity at the surface of each plate, but a blanketing layer of ions builds up and stops it.

But as soon as the two plates of the accumulator are electrically connected (as they would be if a load such as a light bulb or an electric motor were wired up to the cell) this upsets the equilibrium of the cell and a reaction begins at both plates.

Connecting the two plates allows electrons to flow freely from one to the other. Consequently, the lead atoms (represented by the chemical symbol Pb) each give up two electrons and become lead ions with a double positive charge ($Pb^{++} + 2e$, where e is the symbol for an electron). The positively charged ions attract the negatively charged $SO_4^=$ ions from the acid, and the two combine to form lead sulphate ($PbSO_4$). The process continues as long as electrons flow.

This reaction at the negative plate produces two things: negatively charged electrons flowing along the wire (i.e. an electric current) and positively charged hydrogen ions being discharged into the acid solution. Both move across to the other, positive plate by their separate routes. The ions and electrons that reach it are probably not the same ones that set out from the far side, but there is a general movement of ions in that direction.

At the positive plate, two reactions take place. The electrons that reach it through the wire are negative and consequently attract the positive hydrogen ions to the plate. The plate is made of lead dioxide (PbO_2). This, the electrons and the hydrogen ions combine to form lead oxide (PbO) and water (H_2O); the reaction is $2H^+ + PbO_2 + 2e \longrightarrow PbO + H_2O$.

Unlike lead dioxide, lead oxide is attacked by sulphuric acid even when no current is flowing through the plate. So it immediately reacts with the acid to form lead sulphate and more water: $PbO + H_2SO_4 \longrightarrow H_2O + PbSO_4$.

The net result of these three reactions is that both plates change to lead sulphate, and the acid turns to water. When the accumulator has reached this stage no more current flows. It is completely discharged.

The accumulator is recharged by passing electric current

In this diagram of the chemical reactions inside an accumulator, the negative and positive plates are shown on either side of the acid electrolyte, and the wire linking the terminals is at the top.

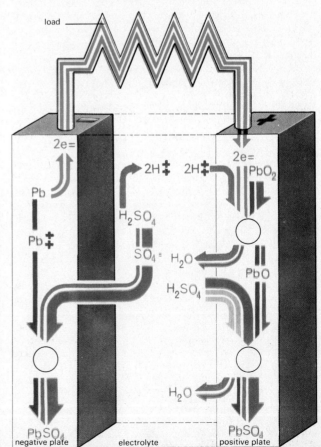

from a generator through it in the other direction. This reverses all the electrical forces, and all the chemical reactions reverse themselves as a result. The lead sulphate changes back to lead dioxide in the positive plate and lead in the negative plate. The water changes back to sulphuric acid.

Accumulators in practice
A lead-acid accumulator, as used in a car, does not in practice consist simply of two plates dipped in acid. Lead dioxide is too brittle, and while pure lead is rigid, the lead that is deposited on the negative plate by the charging process builds up as a sort of metal sponge, which is very fragile. Consequently, both plates need some sort of support.

This is normally accomplished by making the plates in the form of grids of an alloy of lead and antimony (which is tougher than pure lead) with the spongy lead or lead dioxide pressed into the grid. There are several grids in each cell of the accumulator (see below) arranged so that positive and negative alternate. They are spaced a short distance apart by insulators to make the construction more rigid. The fact that there are several grids does not affect their working.

A single *cell*, that is one set of plates immersed in a single container of acid, produces electricity at the comparatively low voltage of 2V. The electrical system of most modern cars runs on 12V; this is provided by linking six cells together in *series* (end-to-end) so as to take advantage of their combined voltage. The six cells are completely separate except for linking bars across the top to carry the current.

A lead-acid accumulator must not be allowed to remain discharged for a long time. This is because the lead sulphate, which is deposited in *microcrystalline* form (i.e. in small crystals), tends to harden into a solid block. Once it has done this it will not take part in any chemical reaction and the plate becomes partly or wholly dead, depending on how much of it is affected. This change is known as *sulphating*.

The state of charge of an accumulator can easily be told by measuring the density of the acid. The more the battery discharges, the more of the acid turns to water and the lighter it becomes. Its density is measured with a HYDROMETER. When the battery is recharged, it becomes warm. Some of the water evaporates, so accumulators must be topped up occasionally.

Other types
The lead-acid accumulator is a simple and durable device but it is rather heavy. Other lighter types of accumulator have been invented. The most important of these is the NiFe (pronounced 'knife') cell invented by Thomas EDISON.

This is so called because the plates are made of nickel oxide (the chemical symbol for nickel is Ni) and iron (symbol Fe). They are immersed in a strong solution of potash.

The NiFe cell is light and robust, but each cell of a battery only produces 1.2V instead of the 2V of a lead-acid cell. As a result, more cells are needed to produce a given voltage. This, and greater manufacturing cost, make the NiFe system considerably more expensive. It is used in portable radio transmitters, because of its lightness.

Other types of accumulator include nickel-cadmium cells and several recently developed types using zinc plates. There is some hope that it may be possible to make these both lighter and more powerful than the lead-acid accumulator, so that they can be used to power lightweight electric cars with a better range and speed than those of today.

ACETONE (see ketone)
ACETYLATION (see organic chemistry)

ACETYLENE LAMP
The acetylene lamp is now obsolete, but was widely used at the beginning of this century as a portable lamp, particularly on cars, motorcycles and bicycles. It burned the same acetylene gas as used in modern oxy-acetylene welding equipment. Acetylene gives a bright light which was much better than the primitive electric lights in use at the turn of the century. But when improved bulbs, reliable dry batteries and cheap dynamos appeared, the acetylene lamp became redundant in a few years.

The gas was not stored under high pressure in cylinders, as it is today. Sometimes it was dissolved in acetone, which made it easier to store under moderate pressure. More commonly, it was made on the spot by dripping water on to solid calcium carbide. The chemical reaction that produced the gas is:

$$CaC_2 + 2H_2O \longrightarrow Ca(OH)_2 + C_2H_2$$
calcium carbide   water   lime   acetylene

In a typical acetylene lamp the carbide was stored in a sealed container at the base of the lamp, either in the form of small chips or in a specially-shaped block. The container had a jet at the top, where the acetylene gas emerged and was lit. There was a reflector behind the flame.

Below: a cross section through a typical acetylene lamp. Water from the domed tank at the top drips down the central tube into a chamber containing carbide grains. The gas produced travels down the diagonal pipe to the burner at the lower right. Heat escapes through vents in the kidney-shaped chimney above the burner.
Bottom: this 1908 Lanchester is fitted with four acetylene lamps.

Leading into the container was a water tube, which was fed by gravity from a tank at the top of the lamp. The speed at which water entered the container was regulated automatically by the gas pressure; if too much water entered, more gas would be generated and the pressure would rise, preventing any more water from entering. There was also a regulating valve in the water pipe, so that the supply could be turned down or off.

In practice, the lamps often had further complications. Some had several burners for front and rear lights fed from a central generator. Others had two generators, the second of which was used only if the first ran out of fuel or broke down.

Acetylene lamps had several disadvantages. One of the most serious was that they were expensive to buy and run. In 1899, a typical bicycle lamp cost 21s, and its carbide refill cost 9s and burned for 5 hours or less. Even at today's prices, this is a lot, and for example considerably more expensive than a modern battery-powered bicycle lamp.

Other disadvantages were that the lamps smelt unpleasant and the jet often became clogged with carbon deposits. Acetylene should burn away completely to produce carbon dioxide and water, but if the flame is badly adjusted it is not hot enough to do this and pure carbon is produced. Lime deposits built up and had to be periodically cleaned out.

In spite of these problems, acetylene lamps gave a powerful light and were used as an industrial light source even after they became obsolete for cars and bicycles. In the United States, some towns had acetylene street lighting instead of the more usual coal gas ('town gas'). In 1909, 290 American towns were lit in this way.

ACHROMATIC LENS

An achromatic lens is a combination of two lenses made of different types of glass, and has considerably less *chromatic aberration* (false colour) than a single lens. All high quality lens systems in modern binoculars, cameras and other optical instruments use achromatic lenses.

A single lens refracts (bends) parallel light and focuses it to a point. The distance of this point from the lens depends upon both the curvature of the lens and the refractive index (light-bending power) of the lens material.

A slightly different refractive index applies to each colour of light. Consequently when white light, which is a mixture of all colours, passes through a simple lens, the various colours are dispersed and are focused at different points. This produces an image with rainbow-coloured fringes, i.e. with chromatic aberration.

Different types of glass have different refractive indexes, so that one type may be used to compensate for the chromatic aberration of another. It is possible to construct a compound lens (two lenses stuck together) with two types of glass of different curvatures fitted into each other; this is free from chromatic aberration for two colours of light. Crown glass and flint glass, which have a different chemical make-up, are the two most commonly used types.

When white light passes through an achromatic lens corrected for, say, red and blue, there will still be a slight chromatic aberration caused by the other colours, such as green. For high-class photographic work, lenses are made with three or more types of glass to eliminate almost all chromatic aberration for white light. These are called *apochromatic* or *process* lenses.

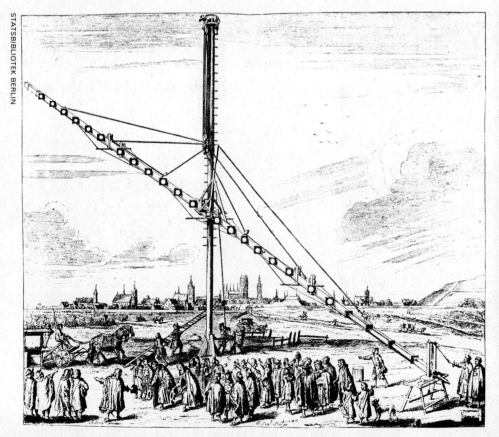

Before the invention of the achromatic lens, by John Dollond in 1758, it was difficult to build powerful refracting telescopes for astronomy. By using a lens with very shallow curves, chromatic aberration was reduced but at the expense of making the telescope extremely long. Some instruments of this type were made and had to be suspended from towers, making them very awkward to use. Sir Isaac Newton in the 17th century believed that it was impossible to overcome the coloured fringes produced by lenses, and he invented the reflecting astronomical telescope with a mirror, which reflects all colours equally, instead of a lens.

Even with well-made modern instruments, chromatic aberration is often seen, particularly when looking through a telescope or pair of binoculars at a dark object against a bright sky. A lens which is well corrected will show barely-detectable apple green and plum red fringes. Poorly made lenses give vivid blue and orange fringes.

ACID-BASE REACTION (see proton transfer reaction)

ACOUSTICS (see sound)

ADDITION REACTION (see chemistry)

ACID manufacture

The quality that distinguishes an acid from other substances is that its molecules contain hydrogen ATOMS which partly split away from the rest of the molecule when the acid is dissolved in water. This causes the hydrogen atoms to become electrically charged IONS with a strong tendency to react with other substances — hence the corrosiveness of many acids. The molecules of 'strong' acids have a great tendency to split.

The main acids manufactured and used in industry are sulphuric, nitric and hydrochloric acid — all of which are strong acids — and acetic acid, a relatively weak *organic* acid, that is, one with a chemical formula related to the complex carbon compounds found in living things.

Sulphuric acid This is a clear, oily liquid with the chemical formula H_2SO_4. It dominates the market for acids.

It can be manufactured directly from sulphur, or from anhydrite (calcium sulphate), a common mineral that is also used for making cement. Other sources include the sulphur-containing by-products of other industrial processes.

The original and traditional method of making sulphuric acid is by the *chamber* or *tower* process, so called because the main reaction takes place in a lead-lined chamber, and other parts of the process in towers. The acid is manufactured by burning sulphur to give sulphur dioxide and reacting this with air and steam in the presence of oxides of nitrogen, which act as CATALYSTS. The reaction is complex, on account of the presence of the catalyst, but basically it is:

$$2SO_2 + 2H_2O + O_2 \longrightarrow 2H_2SO_4$$
sulphur dioxide · water · oxygen · sulphuric acid

The chamber process yields acid of a rather low strength and purity, and its use has dwindled until now only about 2% of sulphuric acid is made by it. It has been supplanted by the more sophisticated *contact* process, which gives very pure acid of any strength. It can even produce the acid in a 'super-charged' form called *oleum* or *fuming sulphuric acid*, which has the chemical formula $H_2S_2O_7$. This intensely reactive and highly dangerous substance turns into ordinary H_2SO_4 when added to water ($H_2S_2O_7 + H_2O \longrightarrow 2H_2SO_4$); if, on the other hand, the water is added to the acid, the reaction boils the water violently, spraying water and acid in all directions.

The outline of the contact process is shown in the diagram.

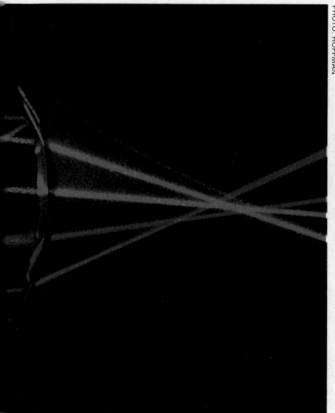

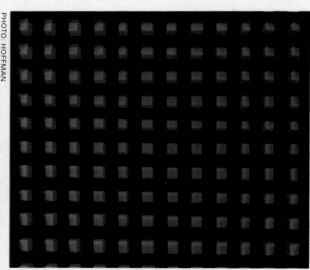

Far left: enormously long telescopes were used in the 17th and 18th centuries in a vain attempt to overcome chromatic aberration. This one was used by the astronomer Hevelius in Danzig in 1670. The square plates with circular holes are not lenses but baffles to blank out the sky around the lens at the far end of the telescope.

Centre: when red and blue light rays are passed through a simple lens, the blue rays are refracted more and focus nearer the lens than the red rays. The 'stray' rays in this picture are caused by reflections off the polished surfaces of the lens.

Above: this photograph of a black and white grid, taken through a simple lens, shows the effect of chromatic aberration.

The contact process produces high quality acid. It is also very economical, since the only raw materials it uses are sulphur, air and water. The catalyst is not used up, though it does need to be replaced occasionally because of impurities in the gas, which 'poison' it.

Below: how the process works. Solid sulphur is tipped into the sulphur melter (upper left) and melted by passing steam through it in a coil. Impurities sink to the bottom and are drained away at intervals.

The molten sulphur is piped to the sulphur burner, where it is burned in air that has been dried by passing it through acid. The sulphur combines with the oxygen in the air to make sulphur dioxide (SO_2).

The reaction produces heat, which is used to boil water in a waste heat boiler. The steam is used to melt more sulphur, and also to power a turbine that drives the air pump.

From the boiler, the sulphur dioxide is passed through a filter and then to a converter, where it is mixed with air and passed over a catalyst.

This turns part of it into sulphur trioxide (SO_3). It also generates more heat, which is used in another boiler.

Next, the gas goes through a second converter, which turns it into almost pure sulphur trioxide. The last remnants of heat are extracted by a small 'economizer' boiler, and the gas is mixed with ready-made sulphuric acid (H_2SO_4) in an absorbing tower to make oleum ($H_2S_2O_7$), a super-concentrated form of the acid.

The oleum is diluted with water to the required strength, after which the acid requires cooling again before it can be piped off to the storage tanks.

In brief, sulphur or sulphur-containing material is burned with dry air to produce sulphur dioxide (the air can be conveniently dried by using some of the acid, which readily absorbs water). The sulphur dioxide (SO_2) is filtered, then passed to a converter, where more air is added in the presence of a catalyst (platinum or vanadium pentoxide) to convert it to sulphur trioxide (SO_3).

This could now be added to water to make sulphuric acid ($SO_3 + H_2O \longrightarrow H_2SO_4$), but the reaction is rather violent so in practice it is added to the acid itself to make oleum ($SO_3 + H_2SO_4 \longrightarrow H_2S_2O_7$). This can then be diluted with water.

Many stages of the process produce intense heat; this is controlled, and also used, in *waste heat boilers*. Water is pumped past the hot chemicals in a closed coil. The heat turns it to steam, which is then used in other parts of the process.

Of the sulphuric acid produced, about one third goes to make fertilizers. Other important uses are in the production of paints, pigments, fibres, detergents and plastics. It is also used for *pickling* (cleaning) steel, making dyestuffs and related products, and manufacturing other acids.

Nitric acid This acid has the formula HNO_3. It is a colourless, fuming liquid when in a pure state, but it is unstable and soon acquires a yellow or red colour when exposed to the air. This is caused by the presence of the gas nitrogen dioxide, which forms as the acid is decomposed by light or high temperatures:

$$4HNO_3 \longrightarrow 2H_2O + 4NO_2 + O_2$$
nitric acid   water   nitrogen dioxide oxygen

The fumes of nitrogen dioxide are extremely poisonous, and the acid itself is one of the most corrosive known. It cannot be stored in a bottle with a cork or rubber stopper,

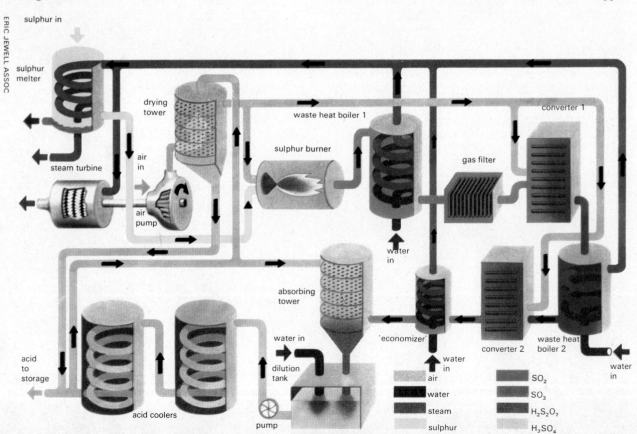

ERIC JEWELL ASSOC

sulphur in

sulphur melter

drying tower

waste heat boiler 1

converter 1

sulphur burner

gas filter

steam turbine

air in

air pump

water in

absorbing tower

converter 2

waste heat boiler 2

water in

acid to storage

water in

dilution tank

'economizer'

water in

pump

acid coolers

air
water
steam
sulphur

SO_2
SO_3
$H_2S_2O_7$
H_2SO_4

since it attacks both these materials. It has to be transported in stainless steel or aluminium containers.

Nitric acid is produced in the laboratory (and was once produced in industry) by treating sodium nitrate with sulphuric acid:

$$NaNO_3 + H_2SO_4 \longrightarrow NaHSO_4 + HNO_3$$
sodium nitrate   sulphuric acid   sodium hydrogen   nitric
                            sulphate   acid

The modern industrial technique is to make the acid from ammonia (itself prepared by extracting nitrogen from the atmosphere), which is treated with air in the presence of a platinum-rhodium catalyst to produce nitric oxide:

$$4NH_3 + 5O_2 \longrightarrow 4NO + 6H_2O$$
ammonia   oxygen (from air)   nitric oxide   water

Further air is then admitted to the 'converter' vessel in which the reaction takes place. This turns the nitric oxide to nitrogen dioxide:

$$2NO + O_2 \longrightarrow 2NO_2$$
nitric oxide   oxygen (from air)   nitrogen dioxide

Finally, the nitrogen dioxide is dissolved in water. With the help of more atmospheric oxygen, it forms nitric acid.

$$4NO_2 + 2H_2O + O_2 \longrightarrow 4HNO_3$$
nitrogen dioxide   water   oxygen   nitric acid

Nitric acid is used for making fertilizers, explosives, dyes and drugs, and also for ETCHING, since it attacks almost all metals. A mixture of one part of nitric acid to three of hydrochloric acid, called *aqua regia,* will even dissolve gold.

Hydrochloric acid
The formula of this acid is HCl. In the pure state it is a gas, but is always used and sold as a solution in water. It is extremely corrosive in either state, and is transported in glass or rubber-lined tanks.

Hydrochloric acid is most commonly manufactured by the ELECTROLYSIS of brine (salt water). The reaction also produces caustic soda (sodium hydroxide):

$$NaCl + H_2O \longrightarrow NaOH + HCl$$
salt   water   sodium   hydrochloric
                          hydroxide   acid

Hydrochloric acid is used for 'pickling' steel before it is galvanized (zinc-plated), for decomposing bones to make gelatine, in the manufacture of dyes and rayon, refining oils, fats and waxes, tanning leather and purifying silica.

Acetic acid
This acid has a more complex structure than the other three mentioned above. Its chemical formula is conventionally written CH_3COOH, which describes its molecular structure to a certain extent as well as its content. It is prepared in various ways, the most important process using naphtha, a cheap and readily obtainable by-product of the petroleum industry.

Acetic acid is the principal ingredient of vinegar, giving it its sour taste (nearly all acids taste sour, but most are poisonous). It is used to make cheap synthetic vinegar, as used by the processed food industry. But this is only a tiny proportion of its main usefulness.

Uses include making cellulose acetate for synthetic fibres, plastics and packaging, vinyl acetate for emulsion paint and adhesives, acetate ester solvents for paint and plastics, synthetic fibres, and pharmaceuticals.

The converter of a modern sulphuric acid plant using the contact process. It consumes roughly 500 tons of sulphur a day. The complex pipework is made of mild steel to resist corrosion. The highly concentrated acid would destroy stainless steel in minutes.

BASF UNITED KINGDOM LTD.

ADHESIVES

An adhesive, strictly defined, is 'a substance capable of holding materials together by surface attachment'. This definition applies to a huge range of glues, pastes, resins and gums.

Science and industry have developed many types of adhesive for various uses, but the basic mechanism of adhesion is still not well understood. At one time it was thought to involve a mechanical attachment: liquid adhesive flowed into pores or cavities in the *adherends* (the materials being stuck), hardened into a solid and thus locked them together. This is now thought to contribute something to the strength of the bond, but not to be its main cause.

Adhesion is now considered to be due to chemical and physical forces of the same kind as those that hold the atoms and molecules of the adherends themselves together, but exactly how these forces are called into play is an active subject of debate among physical chemists.

What is known is that adhesion requires actual wetting of the adherends with the adhesive, so that the detail irregularities of the surface are filled — even the most apparently smooth surfaces are full of irregularities at molecular level.

Design of joints   An adhesive joint of the normal type has five parts, which may be considered as five links in a chain — the joint being as strong as the weakest link. They are: the inherent strength (or *cohesion*) of one material, the strength of the bond of the adhesive to it, the inherent strength of the adhesive itself, the strength of its bond to the other material, and the strength of the other material.

With most types of adhesive, the strength of the bond between adhesive and adherend is stronger than the cohesion of the adhesive itself. For this reason, it is important to keep the adhesive film as thin as possible to make the joint less likely to come unstuck at this point.

The joining surfaces of the adherends must therefore fit together exactly. They must also have a large enough area, and the right shape, so as not to overstress the joint. Adhesive joints resist shear (sideways forces) and tension well, but do not stand up to peeling forces, where there is tension at one edge of the joint that can cause a split to form and spread.

More and more joints in manufactured goods of all types are being made with adhesives instead of more traditional methods such as bolting or welding. This even includes metal to metal joints: recent examples include aluminium chair leg assemblies and certain parts of aircraft, where 'honeycomb' structures of light alloy are bonded between two panels.

In joints of this type, the adhesive cannot normally be used as a direct replacement for the earlier fastening method, and the joint has to be redesigned from scratch. Sometimes the adhesive is used as a supplement to a mechanical fastening: parts are spot-welded together and the space between the welds filled with adhesive to steady the parts against vibration.

It is important to choose the right adhesive for a job. For example, joints between flexible materials must be made with a flexible adhesive. In industry, other factors are also important, for example setting time. It is no use cutting manufacturing costs by using adhesive joints instead of more expensive fastenings if the whole industrial process is held up while everyone waits for the adhesive to set.

Types of adhesive   *Natural adhesives* may come from animal, vegetable or mineral sources. They may be *hot melt* adhesives, which come in solid form, are heated to liquefy them and harden on cooling. They may be *water-soluble*:

adhesives of this type may be in the form of liquids or powders to dissolve in water; either kind remains soluble even after it has dried, so they are not waterproof. The adhesive may also be dissolved in a *chemical solvent* which evaporates faster than water, thus allowing it to set quickly. This type of adhesive is normally waterproof.

The name 'glue' is widely used for any type of adhesive, but strictly speaking only applies to *protein derivatives,* that is, gelatin-like adhesives made from animal or vegetable protein. Scotch glue and similar types of woodworking glue are made by the traditional method of boiling down bones. They are hot melt adhesives. A newer type, soybean glue, is made of vegetable protein. Casein glue is a water-soluble woodworking adhesive made from milk.

Natural starches, cellulose and *gums* from various plants are used to make light, inexpensive water-soluble adhesives. These are much used in the paper industry, and also in the home as wallpaper paste and 'office' paste and gum. The adhesive on stamps and envelopes is gum arabic.

Natural rubber, generally dissolved in air-drying chemical solvents, makes adhesives that are used in industry for glueing rubber and leather, in building for attaching wall and floor coverings, and in drawing offices for glueing paper (because it can easily be removed without leaving a mark).

Natural resins and *bitumens* include asphalt, which is used to bind aggregate (gravel) in road-making and similar applications. 'Marine glue' is a natural resin in a chemical solvent. It is not a true glue, which would not be waterproof enough for marine use. Sealing wax is a hot melt natural resin adhesive.

All the adhesives mentioned above are organic in origin.

There is one inorganic natural adhesive: *waterglass* (sodium silicate) which is used in the paper industry.

Synthetic adhesives are generally called synthetic resins, because the natural adhesives they most resemble are the resin types. There are many varieties including one not found in natural adhesives: the *two-part* adhesive, where the adhesive is mixed with a separate *hardener* or *catalyst* to make it set. Synthetic resins are normally classed as *thermoplastic* (melting when heated) and *thermosetting* (heat speeds hardening).

Thermoplastic adhesives include the *vinyl resins*, a versatile group that stick well to glass and metal, but are also used in many other applications. Polyvinyl acetate (PVA) adhesive is water-soluble and used for woodwork. Other types have chemical solvents or are hot melt types, such as the resin that is sandwiched between two thin layers of glass to make laminated safety glass for car windscreens.

There are several types of *acrylic resin*, most of them two-part adhesives cured by adding chemicals. They are not usually very strong, but are more transparent than other types of adhesive. Objects are often embedded in clear acrylic resin for protection or display. One unusual type is *cyanoacrylate* adhesive, a two-part type that 'cures' to a high strength in a few seconds. This quality makes it useful for production lines.

Cellulose adhesives consist of chemicals derived from cellulose (such as cellulose acetate) in an air drying chemical solvent, and are not the same as the water based natural cellulose pastes mentioned above. They are quick drying and waterproof. Most clear domestic adhesives are of this type.

Thermosetting adhesives include *epoxy resins,* the strongest of all adhesives. Some types will withstand a shearing stress of up to 7000 lb per square inch (500 kg/cm²) in correctly designed joints. Like most thermosetting resins, they are generally supplied in two-part form. Since there is no solvent to evaporate, the adhesive does not shrink as it dries. This makes it suitable for filling the gaps in ill-fitting joints.

Polyester resins are cheaper than epoxy resins, and are therefore suitable for use in bulk. Their commonest use is with glass fibre to make glass-reinforced plastics.

Synthetic rubber is used with chemical solvents to make many types of adhesive. These include the 'contact' or 'impact' adhesives. The pressure sensitive adhesives which are used on adhesive tape are also of this type. Synthetic rubber adhesives are widely used in cars for attaching interior trim panels.

Other thermosetting resins include the *phenolics,* which are available both as chemical solvent types and in thin, solid, pressure-sensitive sheets which are used by the plywood industry for glueing layers of wood together. The *ureas* and *resorcinols* are also used for this and other woodworking purposes. In applications where very high temperatures will be met, *silicone* adhesives are used. *Alkyd resins* are used to make an insulating varnish for electronic components.

Two products that do not fit into any of these categories, but are strictly speaking adhesives, are *solder* and *hydraulic cement* (e.g. ordinary portland cement). Solder is used as a hot melt adhesive for metals where the higher strength of a welded joint is not needed. Cement might reasonably be described as a two-part adhesive where water is the hardener, since wetting it causes it to change chemically into a waterproof solid.

ADSORPTION (see sorption)

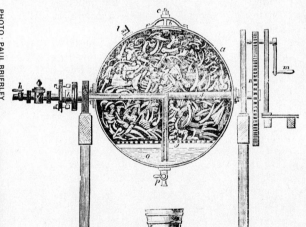

Above: Yardley's extractor for producing glue from bones, a picture from a British encyclopaedia of 1849. The large sphere is filled with bones through the airtight door c and high pressure steam is pumped in through the valve h. The whole vessel is then revolved slowly by turning the geared handle m. The steam and the agitation cause the bones to dissolve into a sticky, gelatinous liquid. After a while the vessel is brought to rest and the liquid collects at the bottom. It is then drawn off through the tap p into the bucket underneath.

Left: a modern 'permanent tack' adhesive, which remains sticky and never sets hard, being tested between two sheets of plastic laminate. This one is based on polychloroprene, a synthetic rubber. Adhesives of this type are useful in industrial processes, since they can be applied to surfaces some time before they are joined, and will give an instant bond when they are pressed together.

PHOTO: PAUL BRIERLEY

RONAN PICTURE LIBRARY

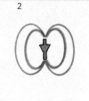

1   2   3

aerial

electric field

aerial

magnetic field

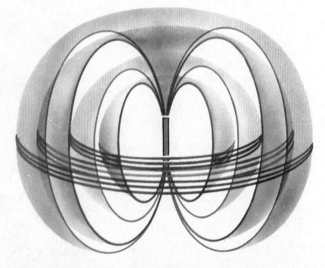

AERIAL [antenna]

An aerial is a device for transmitting or receiving RADIO waves. A transmitting aerial converts the electrical signals from a transmitter (radio, television or radar) into an electromagnetic wave, which spreads out from it. A receiving aerial intercepts this wave and converts it back into electrical signals that can be amplified and decoded by a receiver, such as a radio, television or radar set.

A radio transmitter produces its signal in the form of an alternating electric current, that is, one which oscillates rapidly back and forth along its wire. The rate of this oscillation can be anything from tens of thousands of times a second to thousands of millions of times a second. The rate is known as the frequency and is measured in *kilohertz* or *kilocycles* (thousands of times a second) or, for higher frequencies, in *megahertz* or *megacycles* (millions of times a second).

The oscillating current in the transmitting aerial produces an electromagnetic wave around it, which spreads out from it like the ripples in a pond. This wave, which is shown in the diagram, sets up electric and magnetic fields. The lines of the electric field run along the aerial and those of the magnetic field around it. Both the electric and magnetic fields oscillate in time with the electric current.

Wherever this wave comes into contact with a receiving aerial, it induces a small electric current in it, which alternates back and forth along the aerial in time with the oscillations of the wave. Although this current is much weaker than the one in the transmitting aerial, it can be picked up by the AMPLIFIER of the radio tuned to receive it.

The air is full of radio waves at all frequencies, which the aerial picks up indiscriminately. Each radio or television set has a means of selecting a narrow band of frequencies at any one time — this is what happens when a particular signal is tuned in. Each set can be tuned within a certain frequency range, and will only respond to signals in that range.

Each frequency is associated with a wavelength. This is because the waves, as they radiate out from the aerial at a certain frequency travelling at the speed of light, space themselves a certain constant distance apart. The higher the frequency, the shorter the wavelength (the product of the two being always equal to the speed of light). A transmission with a frequency of 1000 kHz has a wavelength of 984 ft (300 m).

Electricity travels along a wire at a similar speed. It will therefore greatly increase the efficiency of an aerial if its length is correctly related to the wavelength of the signal it receives or transmits. Ideally, aerials are exactly one half or one quarter of the wavelength they receive or transmit.

Receiving aerials inside domestic radios cannot be even one quarter as long as the wavelength, and in any case have

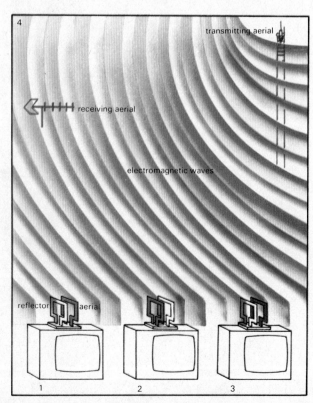

4

transmitting aerial

receiving aerial

electromagnetic waves

reflector   aerial

1   2   3

Top left : an aerial radiates both an electric field (shown in red and blue) and a magnetic field (shown in green and brown). The polarity of these fields changes with the direction of the electric current in the aerial. This results in waves spreading out in all directions (1, 2, 3). The wavelength is the distance from 'crest' to 'crest' of the waves (from one red line to the next). The shape that the two fields take together is shown in picture 4.

Left : the waves spread out from the transmitting aerial and can be picked up by any properly aligned receiving aerial within range. In this diagram, a simple set-top TV aerial with one reflector shows how the 'crest' of a wave strikes the aerial (1) and the reflector a moment later (2), and is then reflected back with opposite polarity to reach the main aerial at the same time as the 'trough' (3).

to work over a wide range of wavelengths. But fortunately, the signal from the transmitter is so powerful that it can be received on a comparatively inefficient aerial.

Types of aerial The same principles apply to transmitting and receiving aerials. The simplest form of aerial is a single elevated wire. This type of aerial was introduced in the early days of radio by Guglielmo MARCONI, who found that by using a wire instead of a small metal cylinder as he had done previously, he increased the range of his transmitter from one hundred yards to one mile.

This type of single element aerial is called a *monopole*. It is connected to only one terminal of the transmitter; the other terminal is connected to earth. This arrangement does not stop current flowing in the aerial; it streams between the aerial and the ground as if across a CAPACITOR, and sets up an electromagnetic field between the two. The ground here is said to be used as a *counterpoise*. Car radio aerials use the car body.

Two-element aerials called *dipoles* are also used. These consist of two rods of equal length (again half-, quarter-, or eighth-wave) set end to end a few inches apart. One rod is connected to each terminal of the transmitter, but they are not connected to each other. The field forms about both rods, linking them. No earthing is needed, since the rods counterpoise each other; they are said to be *balanced-fed*.

A transmitting aerial may be set either vertically or horizontally, provided the receiving aerial is set the same way. Vertically set aerials transmit *vertically polarized* waves, which have little effect on a horizontal receiving aerial (and vice versa). For the best results, the receiving aerial should be set at exactly the same angle as the transmitting aerial.

This *directivity* (sensitivity to angle) of an aerial is very clearly shown in the comparatively inefficient aerials of portable radios. These may be of two types: the *loop aerial,* a long loop of wire wound many times around the interior of the cabinet, and the *ferrite rod* aerial, where the wire is wound around a magnetic material which increases its efficiency. For the best reception, the plane of the loop, or a plane at right angles to the ferrite rod, should pass through the transmitter. The performance of a portable radio or a television with an indoor aerial depends very much on the way it is pointing.

Television detector vans use the directivity of swivelling loop aerials connected to powerful receivers to locate the faint radio signals broadcast by the magnetic coils of a television set. The operator rotates the loop until the strongest signal is received. He can then tell in which direction the set lies by the way the loop is pointing.

Directivity has other uses, too. Reception of a broadcast is often impaired by interference from another transmitter with nearly the same frequency. Medium and long wave radio signals follow the curve of the earth and can travel hundreds,

Right: a TV transmitter mast at Bagshot radio station, Surrey. It also carries microwave 'horn' aerials. Only the top of the mast is a TV antenna. The rest is a supporting structure.

Below: a row of various types of microwave aerial at the Post Office relay station, Ingleby Arncliffe, Yorkshire. The 'horn' aerials transmit narrow beams of radio waves aimed precisely at receivers miles away, making it hard to 'eavesdrop'. For this reason a microwave network has been set up in Britain to carry messages of national importance in emergencies.

or even thousands of miles with comparatively little loss of strength, which can cause serious 'overcrowding' problems.

The shorter wavelengths or very high and ultra-high frequency transmissions (vhf and uhf), which are used for hi-fi radio and television broadcasts, will only travel in straight lines, and stop at the horizon. This means that there has to be a large number of vhf and uhf transmitters to cover a country, which can cause reception problems to someone half way between two transmitters sending different programmes.

Both problems can be solved by using a strongly directional receiving aerial lined up with the desired transmitter. The classic type of highly directional aerial is an ordinary domestic television aerial.

This consists of a half-wave horizontally polarized dipole aerial — the uhf band used in many countries for colour television has wavelengths ranging from 1 m (3 ft) down to 0.1 m (4 in). The dipole is lined up with the transmitter. In front of it (as seen from the transmitter) there is a row of *directors,* which are plain metal rods approximately the same length as the dipole, but not connected to it or the set. Behind it is a row of reflectors, which are similar in appearance.

The directors and reflectors pick up the signal. This causes a slight current to flow in them, so that they re-radiate the signal, though very weakly and with a changed phase, i.e. positive for negative and vice versa.

The nearest reflector behind the main element of the aerial is set one quarter of a wavelength away from it. This means that the 'peak' of each oscillating wave travels past the main element and strikes the reflector slightly later in time, making it one quarter of a cycle out of phase. It is re-radiated instantaneously by the reflector; the changed polarity makes it another one half cycle out of phase, or three quarters of a cycle in all. By the time it gets back to the main element, it has dropped back another quarter cycle, so when it reaches it it is one whole cycle behind, and is thus exactly in phase again. As a result, the reflected waves coincide exactly with the direct waves, and the signal is reinforced.

All the other reflectors and directors are spaced to act in the same way. But they will only have this effect when the aerial is lined up precisely on the transmitter. If it is not, the reflections will travel diagonally between the rods, and therefore through a greater distance. This will make them out of phase, so they will cancel each other out.

A typical rooftop UHF aerial for colour TV reception consists of a ladder-like row of directors — there may be between 6 and 18 depending on the strength of the signal in the neighbourhood — with the main dipole element behind them. Behind this is a *deflector,* an earthed grid which screens out unwanted reflections from other sources.

For the best directivity (needed for radar, radio astronomy, etc.) *parabolic* reflectors are used. These are shaped like the reflector of a car headlamp and focus the waves into a narrow beam in exactly the same way. Horn shaped reflectors are used for *microwave* (very short wavelength) transmitters and receivers, and have a similar effect. With longer waves, good transmitter and receiver directivity can be obtained with an *array* of aerials. This looks like an aerial with a row of directors and reflectors, but in fact all the aerials are 'live' and connected to the transmitter or receiver. The signals of the different members of the array reinforce each other in the same way.

New types of aerials have been developed which include their own transistor amplifier, separate from the rest of the radio. This arrangement enormously increases efficiency.

AERIAL PHOTOGRAPHY

Aerial photography is a technique that can be used to record a huge variety of phenomena on the earth's surface. Its chief uses lie in MAPMAKING and military reconnaissance, but it is also used in surveying, ecology, mineral prospecting, archaeology and many other fields. Since the last war, technological developments have broadened its scope. INFRA-RED film now allows the temperature of objects to be photographed as well as their shape and colour, and SATELLITES allow vast areas to be photographed at once, which has greatly improved WEATHER FORECASTING.

The versatility of aerial photography lies in the fact that by taking a long view of the earth's surface from a high viewpoint, a large number of objects can be shown arranged as if on a plan. This allows comparisons to be made easily, and

Above: when aerial photography is used for military reconnaissance, it is vital to have regular coverage of an area. These two pictures show the German rocket research station at Peenemuende before and after it was bombed by the RAF on the night of 17/18 August, 1943. It was here that early research work and tests were carried out on the V-1 flying bomb and V-2 rocket. Bombing forced the Germans away from large, obvious sites into smaller installations that could be moved. V-2s were completely portable and launched from trailers.

Above right: this EMI 'reconnaissance pod' contains radar and an infra-red scanner as well as an ordinary camera. It is shown fitted underneath a Phantom jet. The huge cameras of earlier years are no longer needed, since improved film and lenses give much finer detail on the pictures. This installation can do far more than a World War 2 camera many times the size.

Right: infra-red 'false colour' photography is a widely used modern technique. Here it has been used on a Florida oil rig to check an oil slick suspected of leaking out to sea. The oil appears as green, unpolluted water blue, and the land red because of infra-red radiation from the foliage.

things to be noticed that would not be apparent from ground level simply because the observer is too close to them.

Early history

Photographs have been taken from the air almost since the beginnings of photography itself. The first aerial photograph known was taken from the basket of a balloon over France in 1856. By the 1880s, photographs were being made from balloons, kites and even rockets in the course of experiments in Europe, and in 1909 from aircraft, both in France and America.

The first practical, rather than experimental, use of the technique was in the American Civil War — it is significant that this was a military use, for aerial photography has been dominated by the demands of military reconnaissance ever since. In 1862, at Richmond, Virginia, the Federal army sent up a photographer in a tethered balloon to take pictures of the

EMI

JOHN HILLESON AGENCY / PHOTO: HOWARD SOCHURECK

opposing positions.

The French were early pioneers in both aviation and photography, and when the war began in 1914, they already had some aerial photographs taken in peacetime of the very places the Germans were invading.

The French photographs provided the inspiration for better aerial photography. J. T. C. Moore Brabazon (later Lord Brabazon), a keen photographer in charge of the British army's air reconnaissance team, experimented with old-fashioned bellows cameras but found them useless. They could not be kept still in the slipstream of an aircraft flying at 80 mph. So he designed a camera suitable for fitting in the floor of an aeroplane — the first purpose built aerial camera.

By the end of the war, these had developed into huge devices with a focal length as great as 6 ft (1.83 m) to give fine detail. Angled mirrors were installed inside the fuselage to 'fold up' the path of the light rays between lens and plate.

Moore-Brabazon introduced the use of a STEREOSCOPE to view pairs of pictures taken from slightly different points, giving an exaggeratedly three-dimensional effect that allowed the heights of objects taken from above to be measured. He also attempted to bring some routine into the taking and interpreting of pictures, so that sequences of events could be followed in successive shots of a place and logical deductions made. At this time, though, the system was still primitive.

Between the wars

At the end of the First World War, the newly developed techniques of aerial photography were applied to peaceful uses — though a certain amount of spying still continued. The main applications were mapmaking and surveying, but there were also other uses.

In Canada, forests being grown for timber were photographed from the air as early as 1921. This was an ideal method of checking on the state of the trees.

Another use of aerial photography was discovered in the United States in the 1920s and 1930s, where the Agricultural Production and Marketing Board regularly photographed farms from the air to check what crops were being grown. In this way, they were able not only to compile statistics, but also to detect false claims made by farmers for the subsidies that were paid for growing certain crops. This unusual peacetime spying made them extremely unpopular.

By 1938, it had become obvious to everyone that Germany was preparing for war. In Britain, the Royal Air Force commissioned the brilliant Australian aerial photographer Sidney Cotton to get as many pictures of military installations as he could without attracting attention.

Cotton had been taking aerial photographs since the early 1920s. His method of tackling the job was most ingenious. First of all, he used RAF funds to buy a Lockheed Electra, a fast civil aircraft which was the latest model and therefore of interest to aeroplane enthusiasts.

He modified this by installing three cameras under the floor; they were hidden by a close-fitting sliding panel when not in use. He also arranged for a stream of warm air to be blown into the camera compartment from inside the aircraft. This prevented the cameras from fogging up or freezing at high altitudes and low temperatures, a problem that had dogged aerial photographers for years.

The next step was to go on a tour of Germany, where his new aeroplane attracted a lot of attention. He often gave joyrides to high-ranking Nazi officers, at the same time photographing the very installations they were in charge of. None of them ever became suspicious.

World War II When war broke out again, Sidney Cotton was given the job of organizing and running the first British photographic reconnaissance unit. Before the end of 1939, he had a Spitfire — the fastest aircraft of the time — fitted with a camera in each wing. It was used to reconnoitre the German frontier from a height of 33,000 ft (10,000 m).

To interpret the detailed and well organized pictures from these missions, he used a WILD PHOTOGRAMMETRIC MACHINE, a highly sophisticated device for taking accurate measurements from aerial photographs. This had been developed in Switzerland before the war and was intended for mapmaking.

The photographic Spitfires and the larger Mosquitos that joined them later in the war were completely unarmed. Removing the heavy guns and armour plating gave them extra speed, height and endurance, which made them almost impossible to shoot down. This advantage lasted almost until the end of the war, when the German jet propelled Me262 and rocket Me163 fighters equalled their performance. Their relative invulnerability allowed them to make regular returns to the same place and thus to keep up regular coverage.

The regularity with which photographs were taken proved vital. Frequent pictures enabled a reference file on a place to be built up, so that troop movements, new buildings and unusual events could all be observed. This enormously increased the value of reconnaissance.

The early successes of Cotton's unit included the detection of V-1 and V-2 launching sites, the forecast of the planned German invasion of Britain and its later abandonment.

When the Americans joined the war in 1941, they adopted a system of photographic reconnaissance closely similar to the British one and achieved comparable successes. In contrast, the Germans never got their system properly organized, which was a drag on their efficiency throughout the war.

Modern techniques Since the war, great advances have been made in photographic techniques. One of the most important of these has been INFRA-RED photography.

Infra-red light behaves just like visible light and can be picked up on a suitable type of photographic film. There are two differences, however. One is that infra-red light penetrates haze much better than visible light, which makes photographs taken from high altitude much clearer.

The other difference is that the amount of infra-red light emitted by an object changes with its temperature. This makes it possible to distinguish between warm and cold water, for example, so that the discharges from factories into rivers can be monitored to make sure they are not overheating the water. The amount of heat absorbed from the sun by living and dead vegetation is different, so the state of a field or forest can be seen at a glance.

Infra-red pictures cannot be printed in infra-red, so 'false colour' film is generally used. This renders infra-red as red, red as green and green as blue. It is insensitive to blue light. Another device, the *airscan thermograph,* uses an electronic scanner similar to a television camera to record infra-red light only, ignoring visible colours altogether.

More detailed information can be obtained with the *multi-band* camera, a device which takes nine simultaneous pictures of the same scene. It is loaded with nine different combinations of film and colour filters.

Pictures can also be taken with side-looking airborne radar (SLAR for short) which has the advantage that it works in complete darkness or fog. This makes it particularly suitable for military use. Unfortunately, the quality of the picture is not

very good, though it is being improved.

All these devices are used for both civil and military purposes. For high-altitude military reconnaissance specialized types of aircraft have been developed, such as the notorious U2, an American spy plane one of which was shot down over Russia in 1962. Its successors can fly faster, higher and farther. Much of their equipment is still secret.

AERODYNAMICS (see hydro- and aerodynamics)

An oblique aerial photograph of the San Andreas Fault, a geographical feature running up the Californian coast from Mexico through San Francisco. The fault is the line along which two enormous continental masses of rock meet. They are in constant slow movement against each other, and the stress caused by the friction between the two sides of the fault gives rise to frequent earthquakes. Aerial surveys of the fault zone allow it to be accurately mapped so that vulnerable buildings can be kept away from the dangerous areas.

AERO ENGINE

The term aero engine can strictly speaking be applied to any aircraft power unit, but it is normally applied to the specialized piston engines used in aeroplanes until they were succeeded by the JET engine. The history of the development of the aero engine has been a struggle to combine high power, lightness and reliability. These qualities were also required in the automobile engine, which was developed at much the same time. But even the earliest aircraft demanded more power than the early motor car industry could produce.

When the WRIGHT brothers came to search for an engine to put into their latest glider in 1903, they thought they could manage to fly with one of only 8 horsepower, provided it was not too heavy. They approached, without success, half-a-dozen makers of car engines. Eventually, they built their own engine and got 12 hp from it, but it was still relatively heavy at 15 lb (7 kg) to the horsepower. Thirty years later, engine designers were aiming at a ratio of 1 hp per pound of engine weight (2.2 hp per kg).

The Wrights' first engine had four cylinders set in line like those of a small car engine. The year after their first flight, a five-cylinder engine designed by the American Charles Manly developed 50 hp at a ratio of 4 lb to the hp.

In the years leading up to World War 1, the French led the field in aero engine design, producing several 50 hp and two 100 hp engines by 1908. But the best of these still only had a power to weight ratio of 3.7 lb to the hp.

The rotary engine Early engines were water cooled, with the cylinders arranged in line or in a V formation as in a car. But in 1907 a new and highly successful type was introduced: the *rotary* engine. In this, the crankcase and cylinders revolved in one piece around a stationary crankshaft. The pistons were connected to a single pivot mounted off-centre, so that they moved in and out as they revolved with their cylinders. The propeller was connected directly to the front of the crankcase and turned with it.

This odd-sounding arrangement worked surprisingly well. It had fewer parts than a conventional engine, and since the cylinders moved rapidly around, they could be air cooled by fins mounted so as to take advantage of the draught. Both factors contributed to make it light.

Rotary engines always had an odd number of cylinders. This reduced vibration, since there were never two pistons moving in exactly the same direction at the same time. The original 1907 Gnome engine had seven, and later types nine.

Other types of engine produced at the time included the Spanish Hispano-Suiza, a design well ahead of its time with eight steel cylinders arranged in a V and screwed into an aluminium block. In the later years of the war this engine yielded, in successive versions, 150, 220 and 300 hp. The Rolls-Royce Eagle, a V12 engine with a broadly similar layout adapted from an original Mercedes design, produced 360 hp in its Mark 8 version of 1917. This was the engine that carried Alcock and Brown across the Atlantic in 1919.

The radial engine Both the Rolls and the Hispano engines had conventional water cooling. This often gave trouble, since vibration and the shock of landing caused the plumbing to break. It was to overcome this problem that a third type of engine was introduced: the air cooled *radial* engine, in which static cylinders were arranged in a circle and cooled by the backwash of the propeller.

This was not a completely new idea, since the water cooled Manly-Balzer engine of 1902, fitted to the unsuccessful

Langley Aerodrome, had also been a radial. The air cooled Anzani engine that powered Blériot's cross-Channel flight of 1909 was also a kind of half-radial, with three cylinders set in a fan shape. The first of the new generation of radials was the 14-cylinder Jaguar engine made by the RAF factory at Farnborough in 1918.

Problems with cooling

Proper cooling is one of the most critical points of aero engine design. Aero engines have always produced far more power for their size than automobile engines of the same date, and have consequently run at much higher temperatures.

These problems led to great rivalry between the designers of air and water cooled engines. Their object was to produce engines that were adequately cooled with the lightest possible system — thus improving the vital power to weight ratio — and at the same time were utterly reliable.

As far as reliability went, the water cooled engine seemed to have all the advantages. Any capacity of radiator could be used to produce the desired temperature.

The temperature of the engine was kept within safe limits by the boiling point of the cooling water, since it could rise no higher than this until the water boiled away completely. Some engines used this feature in *evaporative* cooling systems, where the water was allowed to boil at the engine. The steam was ducted off, re-condensed into water and returned to the engine. The system had been used as early as 1907 in the French Antoinette engine.

In other engines, ethylene glycol (anti-freeze) was used as a coolant, raising the boiling point to 140° C (284°F) to provide an additional safety margin.

The principal trouble with this type of engine was the weight and complexity of the cooling system — it was one more thing to go wrong. Air cooled engines did not suffer from this problem, since their system had no moving parts.

The cylinders were always arranged radially in one or more circular rows. This placed them just behind the propeller, an ideal position for cooling. They were also spaced quite wide apart, so that the outside could be covered with large fins to increase the surface area and thus improve heat dissipation.

Early radial engines had their cylinders completely exposed to the air, but in the early 1930s a shaped ring cowling was added around the engine to improve air flow around the cylinders and reduce the drag caused by the wide, flat-fronted engine.

The main trouble with the air cooled radial was that there was no fixed upper limit on its temperature, so it would overheat very quickly if over-extended. This problem, however, led to the production of high quality heat resistant alloys which made the development of the jet engine possible later on.

Advances in design

The aero engine designers of the 1920s and 1930s had little of today's complex testing equipment using ULTRASONICS and SPECTROSCOPES. They managed, however, to produce reliable engines with ingenious new features by sheer good design and workmanship.

One of the best of these improvements was the *sleeve valve*, which replaces the complex valve gear of a conventional engine with a single tube sliding up and between the piston and the cylinder — it completely encircles the piston. It has ports, or holes, in its upper end. These slide past matching ports in the cylinder head which are connected to the fuel supply and exhaust systems, thus opening and closing them at the correct time. This greatly reduces the number of moving

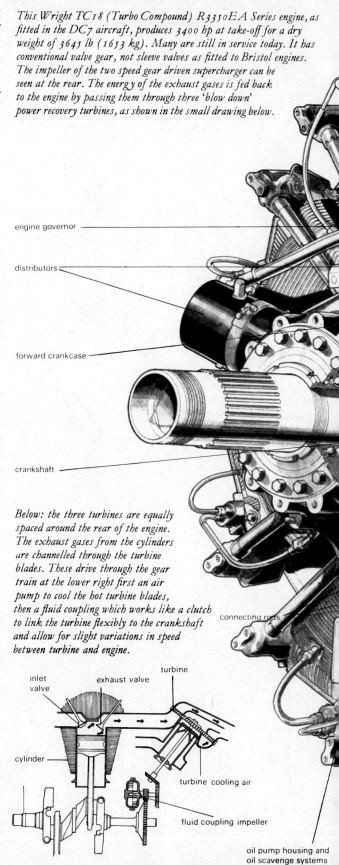

This Wright TC18 (Turbo Compound) R3350EA Series engine, as fitted in the DC7 aircraft, produces 3400 hp at take-off for a dry weight of 3645 lb (1653 kg). Many are still in service today. It has conventional valve gear, not sleeve valves as fitted to Bristol engines. The impeller of the two speed gear driven supercharger can be seen at the rear. The energy of the exhaust gases is fed back to the engine by passing them through three 'blow down' power recovery turbines, as shown in the small drawing below.

engine governor

distributors

forward crankcase

crankshaft

Below: the three turbines are equally spaced around the rear of the engine. The exhaust gases from the cylinders are channelled through the turbine blades. These drive through the gear train at the lower right first an air pump to cool the hot turbine blades, then a fluid coupling which works like a clutch to link the turbine flexibly to the crankshaft and allow for slight variations in speed between turbine and engine.

connecting rods

inlet valve

exhaust valve

turbine

cylinder

turbine cooling air

fluid coupling impeller

oil pump housing and oil scavenge systems

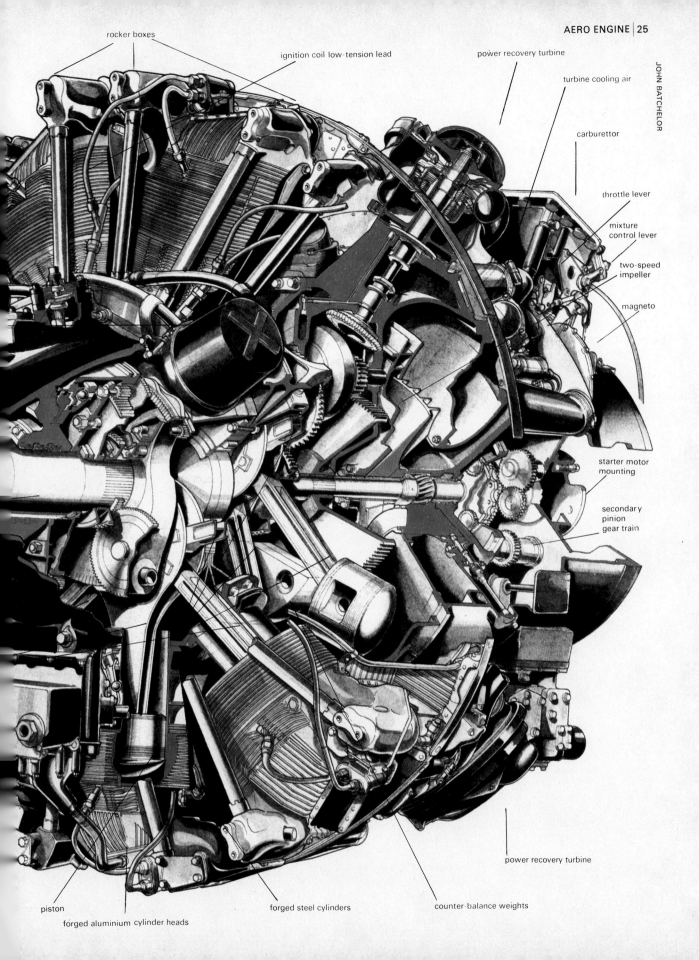

rocker boxes

ignition coil low-tension lead

power recovery turbine

turbine cooling air

carburettor

throttle lever

mixture control lever

two-speed impeller

magneto

JOHN BATCHELOR

starter motor mounting

secondary pinion gear train

power recovery turbine

piston

forged aluminium cylinder heads

forged steel cylinders

counter-balance weights

parts in the engine, particularly as the sleeve can be moved by quite simple machinery set around the inner edge of the ring of cylinders instead of the conventional long train of rods and levers reaching to the outside.

The alloy of which the sleeve is made is vital, because of its expansion as it heats up. If it expands too much it jams against the cylinder; too little and it jams against the piston. Fedden had to consult 60 firms before he found the right alloy.

Many engines had SUPERCHARGERS — compressors to force extra fuel and air into the cylinders and thus improve the engine's performance. These had been used as early as 1910, but were never entirely satisfactory because the compressor needed power to drive it, thus wasting some of the extra power it gave. Several attempts were made to build a *turbo-supercharger* [turbocharger] powered by a TURBINE driven by the exhaust gases, but there was still no alloy that would withstand the high temperature. This was found later.

By the mid-1930s, engines were producing so much power that the PROPELLER was being driven at an excessive speed. The tips of the blades broke the sound barrier and created shock waves that reduced the propeller's efficiency. The difficulty was overcome by gearing the propeller down. The more advanced American engines had variable gearing. By the end of the 1930s most propellers also had variable *pitch* (blade angle) so that they could run efficiently at different speeds.

There was always an incentive for designers to produce

Above: The Wright brothers built their original engine of 1903 themselves. It was a simple four cylinder design similar to a car engine but made as light as possible. Even so, it weighed a total of 179 lb (81 kg) and only produced a maximum of 12 hp. This was a very poor power to weight ratio even for the time, since the earlier Manly-Balzer engine, a five cylinder radial, produced 52 hp and was actually lighter at 151 lb (69.5 kg).

Below: a Rolls Royce Merlin engine, one of the most successful aero engines ever produced. Originally designed in 1934, it continued in production beyond the end of the Second World War, and was even built under licence in the United States. This example, a Mark 60 of 1943, produced 1250 hp. The large domed casing at the rear is a two speed, two stage centrifugal supercharger.

more and more powerful engines. During the 1920s and 1930s it was the glamorous (and lucrative) Schneider Trophy; later it was the desperate need to build fast aircraft in the Second World War.

Among the most famous engines of this long period of rapid development were the British Bristol Jupiter of 1921, a 9-cylinder radial producing 485 hp. This was one of Fedden's designs. In 1926, the American Pratt and Whitney Wasp, another 9-cylinder radial, produced 600 hp, and in 1929 the Wright Cyclone, another American radial 9, 1525 hp.

Meanwhile, Rolls-Royce produced a V-12 water-cooled engine for the Schneider Trophy which gave 2600 hp, though only for a few minutes at a time. This was all that was needed for two successive races, but the basic design of the short-lived engine was used for the famous Rolls-Royce Merlin, which powered the Spitfire, Hurricane and Mustang in the Second World War. The original 1934 Merlin produced only 790 hp, but by the end of the war this had been increased to well over 2000 by successive modifications.

Radial engines included the British Bristol Hercules of 1936, a 14-cylinder two-row radial that gave 1980 hp, and a long series of American Pratt and Whitney Wasp engines, such as the Double Wasp (1937; 2500 hp) and the Wasp Major, an amazing 28-cylinder 4-row radial (1945; 3800 hp).

By this time, the piston aero engine had reached the end of its possibilities. It was used for years afterwards, and still is, but leadership in design had passed to the jet engine.

AEROFOIL

An aerofoil [airfoil] is a body shaped to produce 'lift' as it travels through the air. The most usual example of an aerofoil is an AIRCRAFT wing, but the same principle is used to provide the driving force of the blades of fans, propellers and HELICOPTER rotors. On some racing cars, aerofoils are installed upside down to press the car down, holding it firmly to the road at speed.

Seen in cross section, the upper side of an aerofoil is curved, and the lower side more or less flat. As it moves through the air, its leading (front) edge splits the air it encounters into two streams, one of which passes over the aerofoil, and the other under it. The streams rejoin each other behind the trailing (rear) edge of the aerofoil.

The curved upper surface of the aerofoil is longer from front to back than the straight lower surface. The air stream that takes the longer, upper route must therefore move faster relative to the aerofoil than the stream that goes underneath in order to reach the trailing edge at the same time.

The faster a fluid (such as a liquid or gas) moves, the lower its pressure — this is known as Bernoulli's principle after the 18th-century Swiss scientist Daniel Bernoulli, who discovered it. The fast air stream over the top of the aerofoil has a lower pressure than the slower one under it, and this pressure difference forces the aerofoil up from underneath.

Tilting an aerofoil so that its leading edge is higher than its trailing edge increases the distance travelled by the upper air stream, and so increases the 'lift'. The angle of tilt of an aircraft wing is called the *angle of attack*. The slower an aircraft flies, the greater the angle of attack its wings must have to create enough lift to keep it in the air. The increased 'nose-up' attitude of an airliner as it comes in slowly to land is quite noticeable.

The angle of attack cannot be increased indefinitely, however. This is due to the phenomenon of *laminar flow*. The

friction between the wing and the air flowing over it causes the layer of air next to the wing (called the *boundary layer*) to move more slowly relative to the wing than the air further away. The same effect can be seen in rivers, where the flow near the banks is slower than in the middle.

As long as the flow over the wing remains smoothly laminar, it lifts well. But if the angle of attack is too great, the pressure above the trailing edge of the wing becomes so low that the boundary layer separates from it and the air flow becomes turbulent. As the angle increases, the point at which the boundary layer separates moves nearer the leading edge, and less and less of the wing produces lift. Finally, so little of the wing is functioning that the aircraft 'stalls' and goes into an uncontrollable dive until it regains normal flying speed.

AEROPLANE (see aircraft)

Above: inverted aerofoils hold down both ends of this car at speed. Below: a level aerofoil creates little turbulence (1) but as a plane slows, its nose rises and the boundary layer begins to separate from the top (2). Finally it separates the whole way along (3) and no more lift is produced, so that the aerofoil 'stalls'.

area of low pressure

1

boundary layer separation point

turbulence

2

boundary layer separates at leading edge

3

AEROSOL spray can

Aerosol spray cans have been used as convenient packages for an ever-increasing range of products since they first came on the market in the early 1950s. The enormous variety of products available in spray cans includes whipped cream, caulking compound for sealing the seams of boats, and even the smell of leather.

A spray can is normally made of tinplate with soldered seams, though for products that are stored under high pressure, an aluminium can is used. At the top, there is a simple plastic valve to control the spray. From the bottom of this, a flexible 'dip tube' runs down to the bottom of the can.

The can is filled with the product to be sprayed and the propellant, a compressed gas such as butane or Freon. The gas is partly liquefied by the pressure in the can, but there is a layer of free gas above the liquid. As the can is emptied, more of the liquefied gas vaporizes to fill the space.

The valve is normally held shut by the pressure in the can, and by the coil spring directly below the valve stem. When the push button is pressed, it forces the valve stem down in its housing, uncovering a small hole which leads up through the stem to the nozzle in the button. This allows the product to be forced up the dip tube by the gas pressure in the can. The nozzle is shaped to give a spray or a continuous stream.

To produce a fine mist, a propellant is used which mixes with the product. The two leave the nozzle together and the propellant evaporates as soon as it reaches the air, breaking the product into tiny droplets. The same technique used with a more viscous liquid and a wider nozzle results in a foam. For a continuous stream of liquid, a non-mixing propellant is used, and the dip tube reaches into the product.

A different arrangement is used in cans containing very viscous substances. The product is enclosed in a plastic bag attached to the underside of the valve and the propellant fills the space between the bag and the can. This stops the product from sticking to the sides of the can and allowing the propellant to escape up the dip tube. Cans of this type can be used upside down; an ordinary can must be kept the right way up so that the end of the dip tube remains in the product.

Aerosol cans are filled on the production line by inserting the product, putting the lid and valve on the can and forcing the propellant in backwards through the valve. The bag type can, however, must be filled with propellant through a small extra valve in the base.

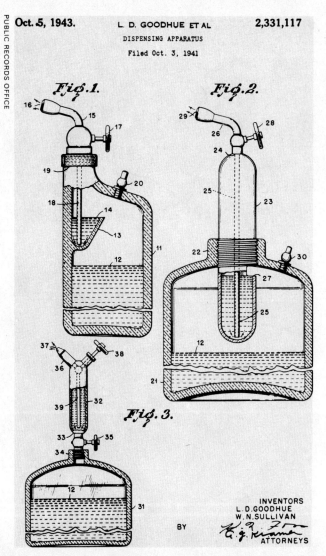

Oct. 5, 1943.

L. D. GOODHUE ET AL

2,331,117

DISPENSING APPARATUS

Filed Oct. 3, 1941

Fig. 1.

Fig. 2.

Fig. 3.

INVENTORS
L. D. GOODHUE
W. N. SULLIVAN

BY

ATTORNEYS

Left: diagrams from the original patent for the aerosol spray, which was filed in the United States in 1941. It differs from the modern type in being refillable and designed to dispense a metered dose, which was tipped into the upper section of the spray by tilting it.

Below: cross section of a typical modern aerosol spray. Gas pressure produced by the volatile propellant forces liquid down the can and up the dip tube to the nozzle when the valve is opened.

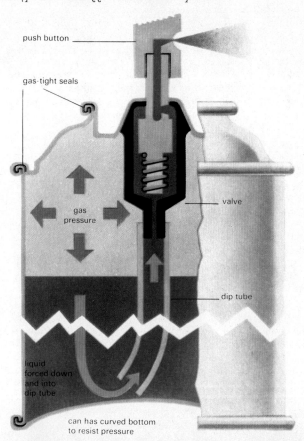

push button

gas-tight seals

gas pressure

valve

dip tube

liquid forced down and into dip tube

can has curved bottom to resist pressure

AGRICOLA, Georgius (1494-1555)

Georgius Agricola was the first man to make a thorough study of mining and minerals. Although he was trained as a doctor, his books on mining were vastly influential.

Agricola was born Georg Bauer in the German town of Glauchau in the Erzgebirge hills. He grew up in an age when books were becoming widespread for the first time, and attended several schools in Glauchau and nearby Zwichau and Magdeburg.

His father was a dyer and woollen draper. Georg did not go to University until he was 20 — 12 to 15 was the usual age in those times. He graduated from the University of Leipzig in 1515 with a BA in medicine and stayed on to teach elementary Greek.

At about this time, Georg Bauer Latinized his name, as was then the fashion among scholars. Bauer means farmer or peasant, for which the Latin equivalent is Agricola.

To further his education, he went to Italy, where he read classical works on medicine and philosophy. He became fascinated by the possible healing powers of minerals, which were abundant in his native Erzgebirge.

He returned to Germany as an MD and took up a post as town physician at Joachimsthal, now Jáchymov, Czechoslavakia, a new town which had grown to be one of the principal mining centres of Europe and famous for its silver. Coins made from Joachimsthal silver were known as *thalers,* from which the word *dollar* is derived.

Its population of 10,000 consisted almost entirely of miners and smelters crowded together. Occupational diseases were widespread. Through his visits to mines and smoky smelting houses, Agricola soon had an excellent knowledge of mines and metallurgy.

Life in Joachimsthal was so demanding that Agricola eventually moved his practice to Chemnitz, a quieter mining town. Here he turned his knowledge to profit, and a judicious choice of mining shares made him one of the 12 richest men in the town.

Agricola's reputation won him an appointment as official historian but his scholarly regard for truth led him to uncover previous rulers' mistakes, and he fell into disfavour. His historical work was not published until 1963.

Agricola's fame rests on his publications on mining and geology. His most important work, 'De Re Metallica', went into minute detail about the techniques of mining in his time. It was published posthumously in 1556 in 12 volumes, and contained not only observations of what he saw around him but also original suggestions about metals and their ores. He gave clear interpretations of the importance of erosion in geology and the origins of ore, and increased by a third the list of known minerals.

The high regard for Agricola even in his own lifetime is revealed by the fact that although he was a Catholic in a fiercely Protestant town, he was several times elected mayor of Chemnitz.

At a time when it was common for industrial techniques to be closely guarded secrets, Agricola believed that processes and innovations should be published and made available to all. He wrote in Latin to gain wide circulation, but 'De Re Metallica' was immediately translated into German and Italian. A century later, the British philosopher Robert BOYLE called Agricola 'the most classick author we have about mines', and his work remained the standard for nearly two centuries.

Left: Agricola is shown in this engraving wearing a doctor's cap and holding a hammer to symbolize learning and geology.

Below: an illustration from 'De Re Metallica' showing a pump for extracting water from mines. It is powered by a treadmill, marked B. Gearing, C & D, transmits the drive at an increased speed to the wheel E, which hauls an endless chain of padded 'pistons' G up a tube and back to its lower end in the mine. Water is drawn up the tube between the pistons and flows out of the top. The padding ensures a watertight fit, the only practicable method in those days.

MICHAEL HOLFORD

PHOTOGRAPHIC LIB OF AUSTRALIA

Top: a model Egyptian wooden plough of about 2000 BC. Basically, it is just a wooden hoe with a shaft connecting it to the yoked oxen. Next from top: this modern Lebanese plough is not much different, but it performs its task perfectly efficiently.

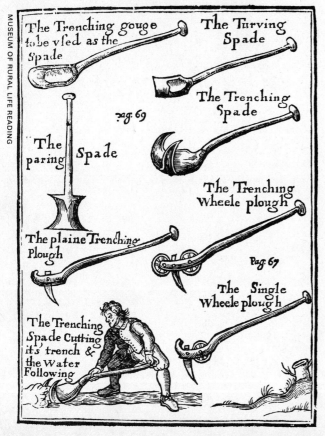

MUSEUM OF RURAL LIFE READING

Left: mid-seventeenth century English digging and trenching tools. All are designed for hand use, without even the help of a horse.

AGRICULTURAL IMPLEMENTS

Agriculture — the growing of crops and domestication of livestock — began in Anatolia around 9000 BC. By 3000 BC, the Neolithic period, it had spread to the great Middle Eastern civilizations, central and western Europe, the Mediterranean basin, China and northern India.

Hunting and farming were carried on side by side. Such simple tools as were required for agriculture were made from the same materials as weapons — wood, flint, bone and horn. These included flint axes for land clearance, wooden hoes and digging sticks for working the soil, and flint or bone handled knives and sickles to harvest the crops. The commonest form of reaping knife had a short wooden handle holding either flint teeth or a single piece of sharp flint. The adze, a woodworking tool, was sometimes used as a hoe.

The evolution of more settled communities together with the discovery and use of metals, such as copper, bronze, and later iron, led to improvements in the basic tools and the development of new ones. Around 2000 BC the straight flint reaping knife was replaced by the sickle with a curved copper or bronze blade, which not only cut more effectively but also was less tiring on the wrist.

In the Middle East there developed the highly productive irrigated cultures on which the great ancient civilizations were built. More intensive farming required more efficient farm tools such as the PLOUGH.

The first plough developed as a two man hoe. It was little more than a forked branch. One man walked in front pulling on a rope or thong attached to it, while another man held the fork as handles and pressed the point into the ground. In Mesopotamia as early as around 4000 BC, a pair of oxen was used to draw the plough. A double yoke passed over the horns of the oxen was bound to the shaft. In both Egypt and Mesopotamia stronger ploughshares of wood or stone evolved, combined with a flat sole behind the blade which dug deeper into the ground and left a wider furrow. Although metals had come into use around 2000 BC, it was not until roughly 1100 BC in Palestine that the first iron ploughshare appeared.

Roman farm tools While the Middle East was the cradle of agriculture, the Mediterranean was the chief source of most farm tools used in Europe. It is uncertain whether the Romans were prime innovators, or whether they merely drew together and improved upon what was already there. Certainly, they contributed irrigation works, corn milling using a water wheel, and the primitive 'vallus' reaping machine. This was an animal driven boxlike machine which was pushed into the standing corn, the ears being removed by a wooden comb device attached to the front of the box.

The Romans had a large selection of tools, many made wholly or partly of iron. These included spades, shovels, mattocks, weeding and drag hoes, billhooks, balanced sickles, long and short scythes (it was not until the twelfth century that the short bar handles were added), pitchforks, and sheep shears, all of familiar design. Threshing benefited by the adoption of a jointed flail although older methods such as the threshing sled — a flint or nail studded board driven by oxen over the threshing floor — and animals treading out the grain were also used.

An important and fundamental difference between the

requirements of the agricultures of the Mediterranean and temperate Europe was in tillage. In the former the aim was to pulverize the surface of the soil to reduce water loss through evaporation during the summer drought. In the latter, where rainfall was more evenly spread over the year, the need was to dig deeper and to turn the soil over, to assist drainage and to improve workability. Therefore temperate Europe required a much heavier plough than the light Roman 'scratch' plough. It had to be equipped with a coulter or knife-like blade to cut into the soil, and a mouldboard to turn the furrow. At what stage such a plough was developed is uncertain; a heavy coulter plough was probably in use before 200 AD but the mouldboard plough may not have evolved until the tenth century.

Farm tools in the 1700s

A list of essential farming tools given by the English agricultural writer, Thomas Tusser, in 1573, is similar to that of Roman times and it was not until the eighteenth century that any serious improvements appeared.

Jethro Tull led the way in 1700 with his seed drill and horse hoe for keeping the soil between the rows clear of weeds. After his invention many people designed seed drills for different applications including some which distributed manure at the same time. James Cooke's drill of 1782 which used gears to turn the seed dropping mechanism was the forerunner of the modern version.

The first practical winnowing machine was invented by James Meikle in 1720. His machine was simple but effective. It consisted of sails fitted to four or more radial arms turned by hand by means of a wheel gear. The artificial wind produced by the sails separated the grain from the chaff. Threshing, too, underwent its first real advancement when Michael Menzies, in 1732, developed an arrangement of flails fixed to a beam and worked by a water wheel.

By 1750 on all but the smallest farms, horse and ox-drawn tools had almost entirely replaced the spade, mattock, and clodding-beetle (so named because it resembled the jaws of a huge beetle — it was used to crush clods). Iron was used widely and most equipment was made on the farm itself, or by village craftsmen, which provided a great variety of individual designs.

Dramatic changes occurred after 1750. The Agricultural Revolution with its new farming systems of tighter crop rotation, and new root and fodder crops, demanded better and more specialized tools. Already the Industrial Revolution was drawing labour away from the land, so labour saving farm machines were needed. In turn the Industrial Revolution assisted the development of farm tools by offering better quality raw materials, engineering expertise, and later the benefits of mass production of complex machinery.

To adjust to varying soil conditions the plough was constantly undergoing changes. In the latter half of the seventeenth century the Rotherham plough was introduced. Modelled on a small light plough from Holland, it required fewer draught horses to pull it. In 1763, James Small improved the plough further with his design for an all-iron ploughboard which turned the furrow more evenly. Other plough designers turned their attention to models which would cut a double furrow.

Developments in the 1800s

Already by 1810 stationary steam engines were used on a few farms to drive barn machinery. Not until the 1840s was a portable engine developed, and the potential of steam as a source of agri-

Top: a fifteenth century Swiss tapestry showing a farm's tasks for November and December. Next from top: steam power completely changed the scale of agricultural machinery. This huge steam thresher of 1905 fed itself with cut wheat, threshed it, bagged the grain and stacked the chaff automatically.

Left: smaller farms, too, could mechanize their work with devices like this chaff cutter. It could be driven by hand or steam, and was used to prepare animal feed.

cultural power realized.

Harvesting required much labour. Consequently more attention was given to harvesting machines in this period. Notable in REAPING MACHINE design was Patrick Bell's invention of 1828. The grain was brought on to the cutter by revolving bars and a row of mechanically operated scissors cut it. The machine was pushed from behind by horses — an unusual arrangement. Three years later Cyrus McCormick in America made a reaper using a knife and cutter-bar principle.

While Britain led the way in steam power, THRESHING MACHINES and horse-drawn field implements, it was the New World — Canada, Australia and above all the United States — which took the lead during the second phase of the machine revolution. A combination of cheap land, large farms and high wages meant an expanding market for labour saving machinery in the Middle West. Most of the harvesting machines in Britain in the 1870s were American. Primitive COMBINE HARVESTERS drawn by mules were already operating in California in the 1890s.

At the Great Exhibition of 1851 British, and at the Great Fair in New York in the same year, American manufacturers displayed a vast array of ploughs, harrows, cultivators, seed drills, drainage tools, steam and horse-powered threshing, winnowing and dressing machines, a wide range of barn machinery, from chaff cutters and root pulpers to oat bruisers and oilcake breakers (all used for preparation of livestock feed), and an impressive selection of dairy tools and utensils.

Dairy machines were not developed until the latter half of the nineteenth century, and then the cream separator came before the MILKING MACHINE. A particularly efficient type, ahead of its time, was the de Laval cream separator of 1879. The milk was placed in a metal bowl which was made to revolve at speeds of around 4000 rpm. The skim milk was forced to the sides and removed from the top while the cream remained in the bottom of the bowl. Cream separators had been known for some time in Denmark, Sweden and Germany but were not as practical.

An American milking machine was demonstrated as early as 1862. It used four elastic tubes connected to an exhaust apparatus and a reservoir, and milk could be drawn at the rate of a gallon a minute. The patent for this milking machine was snapped up for £5000 by a firm in Birmingham (England) but little more was heard of it. During the 1890s more effort was put into designing efficient milking machines, one such machine being patented by William Murchland, a sanitary engineer and plumber. It was a continuous suction machine, worked by gravitation with the vacuum created by water. Despite the claims of success, it was not until after the First World War that milking machines were satisfactory.

The next major phase of farm mechanization awaited the development of a more efficient and flexible prime mover than the steam engine, which, because of its great size and unfavourable power-to-weight ratio, was unsuitable for fieldwork. The breakthrough came in the 1890s when Herbert Stuart and Charles Binney patented the first stationary paraffin-oil [kerosene] engine.

Farm machinery in the 1900s

During the next seventy years the INTERNAL COMBUSTION ENGINE replaced man, horse and steam, to become the chief source of energy. The history of the TRACTOR began with the 'Ivel' tractor of 1904. America was chiefly responsible for the development of an efficient tractor and by the 1920s were mass producing them for an international market. By the 1930s, pneumatic tyres and power take-off to drive separate machinery became standard equipment and a wide variety of suitable tractor fittings were available.

Since the Second World War diesel fuels have replaced paraffin and petrol [kerosene and gasoline]. Larger and more versatile tractors capable of performing an increasing range of farm tasks are available. Other machines which have become widely used are the combine harvester, corn drier, milking machine, stationary oil engine and electric motor, all of which, though invented before 1914, were little used at the time.

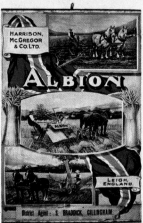

Above: McCormick hay and cereal harvesting machinery made by the American firm of International Harvester, who exported widely to Western Europe from the nineteenth century to the present day. It was named after Cyrus McCormick's original reaping machine of 1851.

Left: A British advertisement of about 1900 for 'Albion' self binding reaping machines. The patriotic name and the flag reflect local resistance to the flood of American imports.

AIRBAG

The airbag, also sometimes known as the Safety Air Cushion (SAC), is a device invented and designed in the United States as an alternative to the car seat belt for protection of passengers in a road accident.

Injuries in accidents tend to be caused not so much by the physical collapse of the vehicle as by the sudden deceleration throwing the occupants around, possibly through the windscreen [windshield]. Seat belts undoubtedly save lives in this situation, provided they are worn, which many people forget or refuse to do. Legislation in the USA requires cars from 1976 onwards to be fitted with *passive* passenger protection that will operate automatically in the event of an accident, rather than just the *active* devices that require action from the occupants before they work, such as seat belts.

The airbag is a strong inflatable neoprene coated woven nylon bag. When not in use it is deflated, rolled and stored beneath the vehicle's instrument panel. An air distribution system is linked to a cylinder of compressed air with a sensing device to determine when the car is involved in an accident.

This sensing device is an ACCELEROMETER which is pre-set to open a valve and release the compressed air when a violent deceleration takes place.

When the device is triggered off, the compressed air inflates the bag in rather less than one tenth of a second. This prevents the occupants from crashing into the dashboard or steering column.

The bag is designed with porous panels that allow air to pass through them slowly. After the inflation of the bag, it immediately begins to deflate, enabling the passengers to leave the vehicle or be rescued.

To prevent what is known as 'submarining', where the person tends to slide beneath the instrument panel, the bags are designed so that the legs and knees, as well as the torso, are restrained.

Airbags can also be provided for the vehicle's rear seats, but these are less important since the occupants of these seats are at much less risk of injury than those in the front.

Many safety experts are opposed to airbags, and believe that their use will be more dangerous than warranted by the injuries they prevent. When inflated, they rob the driver of control of the vehicle, possibly leading to further impacts. Accidental inflation could be disastrous, and the noise of the explosion required to set off the airbag could cause considerable shock and even rupture the occupants' eardrums.

Airbags have not always performed well in tests, though a 1000-car trial involving 8.1 million miles (13 million km) of travel has been carried out with some success in the United States. But the system may never come into use if some other more acceptable form of passive restraint can be found.

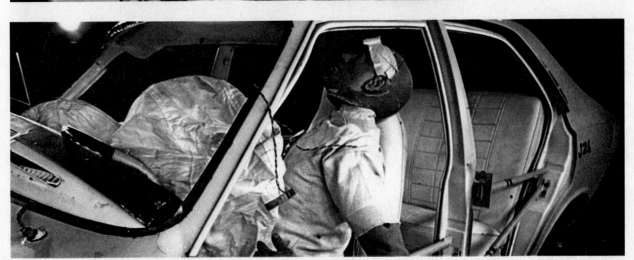

Above left: not all airbag tests are successful. In this 1971 trial the bag inflated a tiny fraction of a second too late. The dummy 'driver' (on the near side) has already crushed his chest on the steering wheel by the time he hits the airbag, and it only serves to bend his neck back at a sharp angle.

Below: as the airbag deflates, the driver falls back against his seat. But in real life, he would probably already have smashed his ribcage, and the airbag itself might even have broken his neck.

AIR CONDITIONING

Air conditioning is the creation of an artificial climate, making it possible to maintain constant, pleasant conditions inside buildings and provide a steady flow of purified air.

In cities, sealed double-glazed windows can be used so that noise and dust can be excluded, and a quiet, pleasant environment can be produced.

With air conditioning, building designers are no longer tied to windows as a source of light and air, and more use can be made of large internal areas, 'landscaped' with plants and fountains, and attractively lit.

Air conditioning is essential in underground spaces, cinemas and theatres, crowded shops, hospitals, tall office buildings, and in many industrial processes which are sensitive to atmospheric conditions.

Methods used

Air is purified, cooled or heated, humidified or dried, according to the need, by the air conditioning plant and circulated through the building by means of ducts, which may be of metal or may be formed out of the structure itself.

There are various stages in a large air conditioning plant: not all plants include every component, and in the smallest air conditioning unit the components are combined in one casing not much larger than a television set.

Air first enters a section where it mixes with re-cycled air from the building — only a certain proportion of fresh air is needed. Next, the mixed air passes through a filtering section, which may be in two stages. The first stage takes out coarse dust, and will be a fibrous medium, rather like cotton wool, either in the form of a screen of individual filter 'cells' which can be replaced when they become dirty, or an electrically

driven roller screen. Following this is the second stage filter which is generally an electrostatic type and removes the finer particles such as cigarette smoke. In this, a high voltage is used to charge incoming dust particles which are then attracted to a grid of oppositely charged plates.

The air temperature is controlled by passing the air through two tube banks. One is supplied with hot water or steam, and the other with chilled water or a refrigerant fluid. Inside the room to be ventilated is a temperature sensor — usually an electrical resistance thermometer — which is set to the desired value. The difference between the required and the actual temperature automatically determines whether the heating or cooling tubes are used.

The next stage is the odour filter, made of activated carbon, a substance which is capable of directly absorbing odour molecules from the air. This needs to be reactivated by heating from time to time to drive off the absorbed material.

Finally, moisture is added to produce the desired humidity, either by injecting steam into the air or by spraying a mist of very fine water droplets. This too is controlled from a sensor inside the room, the electrical resistance of which varies with the humidity. If moisture has to be removed from the air, the usual method is to arrange for it to be both cooled and then re-heated if necessary at the temperature control stage. The moisture will condense on the cooling tubes.

The air is normally moved through the system by a centrifugal fan, the rotor of which resembles a paddle wheel. Air enters at the centre and leaves around the edge of the wheel. This type of fan can move large volumes of air despite the appreciable drag of the plant and ducting.

Silencers are always placed after the fan to prevent the

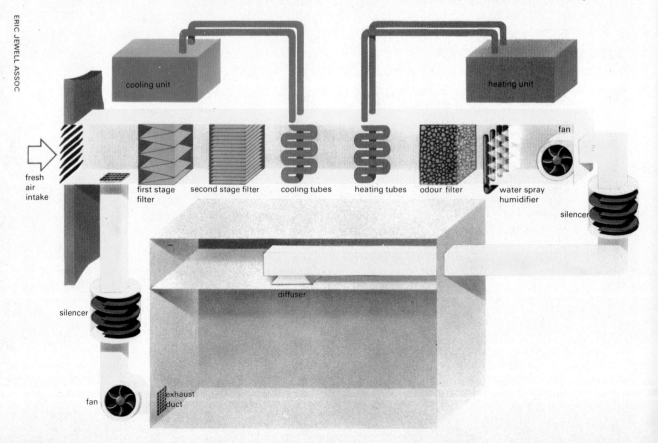

fresh air intake — first stage filter — second stage filter — cooling tubes — heating tubes — odour filter — water spray humidifier — fan — silencer — cooling unit — heating unit — silencer — diffuser — fan — exhaust duct

noise of the plant from reaching the room. These usually consist of a labyrinth of sound absorbing material.

Air is finally delivered through metal ducts to the room 'diffusers'. These take various forms, such as long slots or grilles in the walls close to the ceiling, vaned outlets flush with the ceiling, or perforated sections of the ceiling itself.

Air conditioning systems

The same principles are used from the smallest to the largest system. Small room units contain a simple washable filter, refrigerating compressor, and electric air heater.

More powerful units are made to supply larger rooms, and frequently the refrigerating section (compressor and condenser) is placed outside the building.

For large buildings there are three main systems: *all air, air-water,* and *all water.* In the first, the plant supplies all the air that is needed at a fixed temperature. Local duct heaters are needed in different rooms or zones of a building to give final temperature control. An alternative is to have two ducts, one carrying cool air, the other warm air. The two air streams are blended, as in a mixing tap, to give the required temperature. In the 'variable volume' system, the temperature is regulated by controlling the amount of air supplied instead of its temperature.

In the air-water system, the central plant only delivers the minimum fresh air needed for ventilation. Each room then has a separate heating and cooling unit using heated or chilled water.

In the all water system, only the heating or cooling water is supplied from the central plant, and fresh air is brought in through individual ventilators in each room.

The air-water and all water systems can use smaller ducts,

are more economical, and run quieter, but are less efficient than the first method, in which all the air is constantly being conditioned.

Air conditioning today

Air conditioning is being used widely at the moment for office blocks, shops, supermarkets, restaurants, and entertainment centres, where the main problem is to keep the building cool in summer. Temperatures in modern buildings can become uncomfortably high through heat from lights, crowds of people, and sunshine through large windows. Even the relatively cool English summer, sunshine through large windows can raise room temperature to an equivalent of over 90°F (32°C) with only 60°F (16°C) outside.

The heat from artificial lighting is sometimes sufficient to keep a building warm in winter, and some buildings have been specifically designed to do just that: the hot air generated by the lights is picked up and returned to the plant.

In medicine, air conditioning is essential for the operating theatre. In this case the air must be sterile and must keep the area around the operating table free from contamination. In industry, air conditioning is needed to control the environment to a process or product. In so-called 'white' rooms, for example in the manufacture of transistors, the atmosphere is cleaner than ever occurs in nature.

The largest single space ever air conditioned is the vehicle assembly building at Cape Canaveral in Florida: 525 ft (160 m) high and nearly 500 ft (150 m) square. The cooling power is sufficient to turn 7500 tons of water into ice in a day.

Ideas for the future of air conditioning include the heating and cooling of domed cities, and the production of a living environment in underground dwellings.

AIRCRAFT

All heavier-than-air craft from a glider to a jet airliner rely on the application of mechanical energy to the air around to give an upward thrust, maintaining the craft in the air against gravitational forces. This idea is the same for AUTOGIROS, HELICOPTERS, VERTICAL TAKE OFF aeroplanes, and anything that might be described as an aircraft as opposed to an airship, which derives its lift by being lighter than the air it displaces.

In a glider, the energy is provided by a towing plane or a launching winch. The wings have a cross-sectional shape known as an AEROFOIL to derive lift from the forward motion, while a tailplane and fin give the machine added stability and let the pilot control the direction of flight. As soon as no further energy is supplied, the glider begins to sink, and must always come back to earth despite rising air currents — 'thermals' — that might give temporary respite.

To maintain a heavier-than-air craft aloft requires a continuous input of energy — some means of maintaining the forward motion against wind resistance. Engine-driven propellers, jets or rockets supply the necessary thrust for this and for take off from the ground.

Typical layout

The shape of aircraft has scarcely changed at all since the early years of this century, though some odd shapes have appeared since the advent of supersonic flight, and there have always been aircraft designers who have preferred a non-conformist approach. Basically an aircraft has a cigar-shaped fuselage for carrying crew, freight or passengers, on which is mounted a wing somewhere near the middle and a tailplane at the trailing end with a vertical tail fin.

Added to this will be one or more engines mounted almost

AIR CONDITIONING ADVISORY BUREAU

Left: schematic diagram of a typical 'all air' system such as might be used for a large building — only one room is shown here for simplicity. Air leaves the room through an exhaust duct (bottom left) and is mixed with fresh air from outside before being passed through two filters, cooling and heating tube banks, an odour filter and a humidifier. It is then returned to the room through a silencer.

Above: a small 'through the window' air conditioner of the type used for a single room, with the cover removed to show the mechanism. It contains most of the elements of the larger system on a reduced scale: top left, a tube bank; directly below it, a centrifugal fan; bottom and right, the compressor of the refrigerating unit; and top right, the electronic circuitry of the thermostat. The filters are out of sight. No silencers are fitted on account of the lack of space.

anywhere, ranging from inside the fuselage itself to the very tips of the wings.

With this layout, lift will usually be derived entirely from the wings so the centre of lift of the wing will normally correspond to the centre of gravity of the aircraft.

Usually the main wing will not form a continuous horizontal line, but will be divided in the middle with the tips raised by a small amount relative to the centre to give what is known as dihedral. Without this there would be nothing to keep the main axis of the wing horizontal during normal flight. As it is, dihedral results in greater lift from the lower wing when the aircraft tilts, thus producing a tendency to restore the wing to a horizontal mode.

The actual lift produced by a wing will vary with the speed of the plane. The faster it goes, the more lift will be produced; this is why aircraft have to attain a considerable speed on the ground before they acquire enough lift for take off.

At the same time higher speeds involve more wind resistance — more drag — so jets and other high-speed aircraft have thin wings to reduce drag. If a plane slows down to below what is known as stalling speed, it literally falls out of the sky, the lift being insufficient to keep it horizontal. With thin wings the stalling speed tends to be higher than with thick wings, so jet aircraft require higher take off and landing speeds.

It would be difficult to control a plane if these factors could not be varied. Jet aircraft would need enormously long runways because of their high minimum speeds, while if these factors were taken care of through thicker wings, their maximum speeds would be severely cut.

Thus a device known as the flap has been developed to modify the wing section so that lift can be changed by the pilot. Part of the trailing edge of the wing, and sometimes the leading edge as well, is hinged downwards to exaggerate the aerofoil section and give more lift at lower speeds. The hinge is often arranged to open a slot between wing and flap through which air can flow to reduce turbulence. Fully extended flaps considerably increase drag, slowing the aircraft. This effect can be increased on some aeroplanes by opening out transverse flaps in the tops of the wings or elsewhere called air brakes.

Control

Once an aircraft is in the air, it has to be capable of moving in three ways: in pitch — up and down; in yaw — side-to-side; and in roll.

Pitch is controlled by hinged surfaces on the trailing edge of the tailplane known as elevators. Moving these upwards curves the tailplane into an inverted aerofoil section, resulting in downward pressure on the tailplane and hence a tendency for the aircraft to adopt a nose-up or climbing attitude. Turning the elevators downwards has the opposite effect.

Yaw is controlled by a flap on the tail fin known as the rudder. If the rudder alone is used the aircraft slews sideways, but this way of turning is inexact and badly controlled. There is no counteracting horizontal force to prevent the aircraft continuing to turn regardless of the pilot's wishes. Additionally, the horizontal centrifugal forces would throw passengers and crew towards the outside of the turn.

By moving the ailerons, control surfaces at the wing tips, the aircraft can be made to bank or roll inwards at the same time as the rudder turns it, so that the aircraft tilts towards the centre of the turn like a bicycle. This is a more stable and comfortable way of turning.

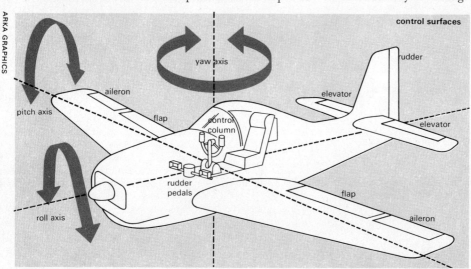

Left: an aircraft has three sets of control surfaces, which tilt it about three axes. The ailerons, which are moved by turning the control column, cause it to roll. The elevators, worked by moving the control column forward or back, cause the aircraft to pitch (point its nose down or up) and thus to dive or climb. The rudder, worked by the rudder pedals, makes it yaw or swivel. A normal banked turn is executed by simultaneously yawing the aircraft and rolling it toward the inside of the turn. This inward tilt gives the aircraft stability as it turns.

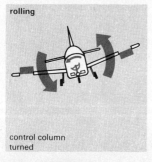

rolling

control column turned

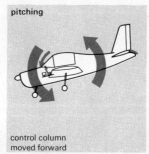

pitching

control column moved forward

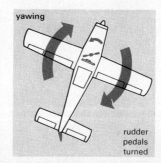

yawing

rudder pedals turned

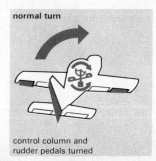

normal turn

control column and rudder pedals turned

In early aircraft the control surfaces — ailerons, elevators and rudder — were moved by the unaided exertion of the pilot through control wires. With today's high speed aircraft, the forces on the control surfaces are much too great for this, and so they are now generally moved by hydraulic cylinders, operated by the pilot through SERVO MECHANISMS. The arrangement works in a similar way to the power steering on a large car. This power assistance makes the controls of a modern aircraft very light, yet they are set to resist the pilot's action just enough to give him an indication that the surfaces are responding properly.

To move the elevators, he moves his control column backwards and forwards; to move the ailerons, he turns the control column. The rudder is activated by two pedals, leaving the hands free to operate the other control surfaces at the same time for banked turns.

Variations in shape

Though the layout of conventional aircraft should remain the same for many years to come, there are now many other types made for specific purposes. Chief among these is the SUPERSONIC aircraft which generally has wings of a delta shape to cut down drag to a minimum and avoid problems with the shock wave caused by supersonic flight. Frequently such aircraft have no tailplane. The ailerons duplicate as elevators, and are known as 'elevons'.

Supersonic aircraft inevitably present a compromise in design because their shape differs from that of subsonic types, yet they have to fly subsonically as well. Inevitably, the result is an aircraft that is inefficient both subsonically and supersonically. To get around this problem, the swing-wing concept has emerged. For subsonic flight, the wings stick out

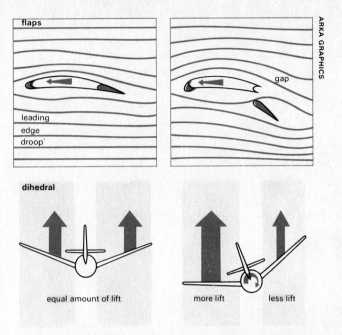

Top: flaps are mounted at the trailing edge of the wing. Their action is sometimes assisted by a leading edge 'droop'. Lowering them adds to the effective area and camber of the wing so that it develops more lift at low speeds. The small airflow through the gap between flap and wing smooths out turbulence caused by the exaggerated camber. Next from top: dihedral, an angling of the wings, causes the lower wing to create more lift when the aircraft tilts, thus righting it.

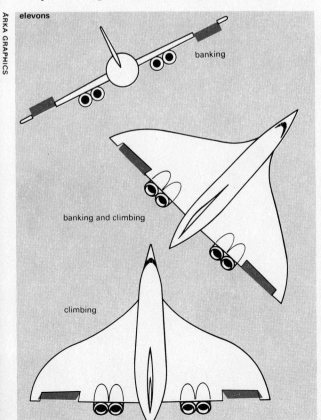

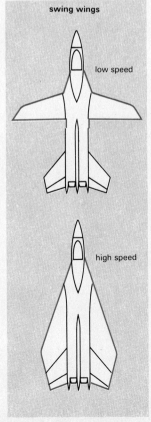

Far left: a delta winged aircraft has no separate tailplane, and so cannot have separate elevators and ailerons. For this reason it has elevons, single control surfaces which perform both functions. To roll the plane, one elevon is raised and the other lowered. To make it climb, both are raised. For a climbing turn, one elevon is raised and the other remains level. The rudder would also be used in this manoeuvre.

Near left: Variable geometry or 'swing' wings are found on many modern supersonic planes. At low speeds, where the maximum amount of lift is needed for take off and landing, the wings are extended sideways. At high speeds, where straight wings would create too much lift and cause problems with the supersonic shock wave, they are folded back to the tailplane to give a deltalike profile. Control is through elevons mounted on the tailplane; there are no ailerons.

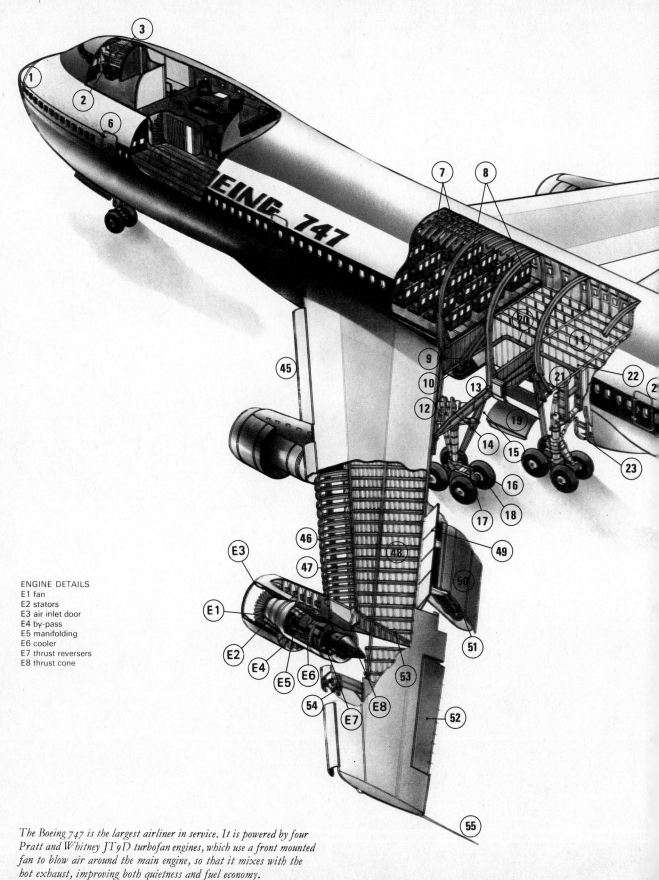

ENGINE DETAILS
E1 fan
E2 stators
E3 air inlet door
E4 by-pass
E5 manifolding
E6 cooler
E7 thrust reversers
E8 thrust cone

*The Boeing 747 is the largest airliner in service. It is powered by four
Pratt and Whitney JT9D turbofan engines, which use a front mounted
fan to blow air around the main engine, so that it mixes with the
hot exhaust, improving both quietness and fuel economy.*

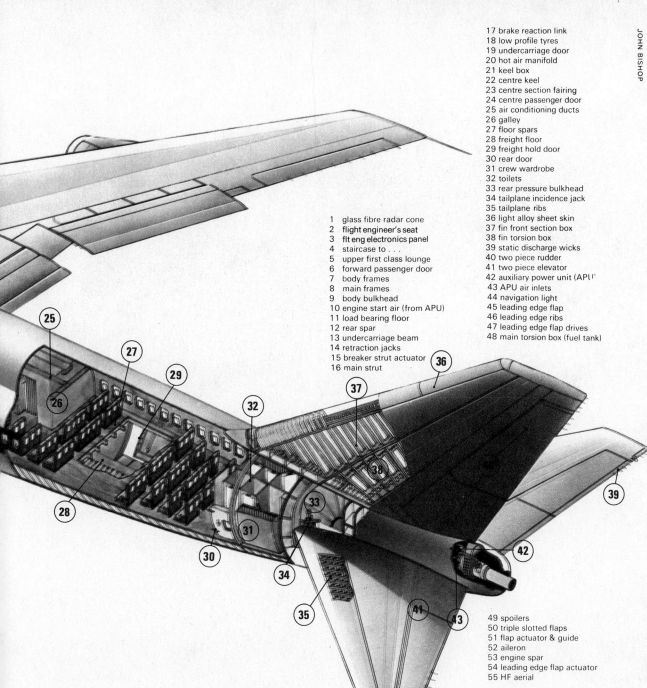

17 brake reaction link
18 low profile tyres
19 undercarriage door
20 hot air manifold
21 keel box
22 centre keel
23 centre section fairing
24 centre passenger door
25 air conditioning ducts
26 galley
27 floor spars
28 freight floor
29 freight hold door
30 rear door
31 crew wardrobe
32 toilets
33 rear pressure bulkhead
34 tailplane incidence jack
35 tailplane ribs
36 light alloy sheet skin
37 fin front section box
38 fin torsion box
39 static discharge wicks
40 two piece rudder
41 two piece elevator
42 auxiliary power unit (APU)
43 APU air inlets
44 navigation light
45 leading edge flap
46 leading edge ribs
47 leading edge flap drives
48 main torsion box (fuel tank)

1 glass fibre radar cone
2 flight engineer's seat
3 flt eng electronics panel
4 staircase to . . .
5 upper first class lounge
6 forward passenger door
7 body frames
8 main frames
9 body bulkhead
10 engine start air (from APU)
11 load bearing floor
12 rear spar
13 undercarriage beam
14 retraction jacks
15 breaker strut actuator
16 main strut

49 spoilers
50 triple slotted flaps
51 flap actuator & guide
52 aileron
53 engine spar
54 leading edge flap actuator
55 HF aerial

straight from the fuselage to produce adequate lift but for supersonic flight they are swept back to form a delta shape. The mechanical problems of hinging a wing for this purpose are considerable, but several types are now flying.

Another aircraft type developed for a specific purpose is the VTOL (vertical take off and landing) aircraft. Strictly speaking the helicopter, deriving lift from an overhead rotor comes into this category, but normally it implies a conventional aircraft that has some additional system for getting it off the ground.

The simplest VTOL aircraft incorporate downward point-ing jet engines that provide lift but contribute nothing to forward motion, this being achieved with horizontally mounted engines.

Others, such as the British Hawker Siddeley Harrier, deflect normally horizontal jets downwards to provide lift. Some propeller driven types are planned where the wings, with the engines mounted on them, are pivoted to allow the oversize propellers to act as rotors.

None of these arrangements excels in terms of efficiency because so much energy has to be dissipated in merely lifting the aircraft's dead weight, but they have good prospects for aircraft that can operate without airfields or can climb straight up to restrict the noise around airports. The armed forces find VTOL an attractive proposition because of the inherent flexibility of such aircraft — vital, for example, in jungle warfare.

A compromise type, STOL (short take off and landing) offers similar, though more restricted advantages at lower cost. So far, most STOL types have been light aircraft with large flaps and other special control surfaces to give high lift at low speeds. There are plans for larger types to be developed for international passenger transportation, and these again will offer a partial answer to the noise problem around airports.

Construction The construction of all aircraft from simple glider to swing-wing supersonic craft has to be carried out with one principal aim in view: to reduce weight as much as possible. Primitive types at the turn of the century adopted a wooden or steel tubular frame covered with canvas or similar material to provide the required aerodynamic surfaces. Such construction methods are still used for some simple light aircraft, though the canvas may also be replaced by glass fibre materials or aluminium sheet.

But for faster high-powered craft, where dynamic forces are involved, such constructional practice would be unsuitable. Most larger aircraft use a reinforced monocoque construction, in which the outer shell takes a lot of the stress but is backed up by a suitable frame of light alloy. The shell is sometimes made of solid light alloy but nowadays tends to be a sandwich of two thin layers glued to a metal 'honeycomb' mesh to give high stiffness with low weight. The aim here is to produce a material akin to corrugated cardboard in cross-section.

For supersonic aircraft, where the stress problem becomes even more acute, wings and other components have to be made by machining outer skin and frame together from solid pieces of alloy. Though giving the strength and heat resistance that are necessary, this method is very expensive and has contributed considerably to the high cost of, for instance, the Concorde project. It seems likely that it will be reserved strictly for military types in future.

For the last fifty years or so, the shape of the aircraft has been largely dictated by military requirements, each nation trying to make its warplane technology superior to that of its potential enemy. Commercial design has lagged behind. But as air travel becomes more widespread and aircraft grow more expensive, commercial design requirements are becoming different. It is expected that the STOL aircraft will come to dominate the commercial market by the end of this century, while VTOL and supersonic aircraft will remain mainly in the military sphere.

AIRCRAFT CARRIER (see warships)

AIRCRAFT HISTORY

The aeroplane had a long period of gestation. Apart from its lack of a suitable engine, progress was hampered in the beginning by too much attention to bird flight. This led to a great deal of wasted effort on flapping-wing machines, known as ornithopters, although as early as 1804, Sir George Cayley had flown a model glider and, before he died in 1857, had flown at least two full-sized gliders with someone on board. Many of the early experimenters also made the mistake of concentrating on inherent stability in their aircraft instead of on controllability. Even Otto Lilienthal, who made gliding

Below: Wilbur Wright's first flight in Europe, a picture of 1908.
Right: poster for the first ever aviation fair in France in 1909.

RONAN PICTURE LIBRARY

Henson and Stringfellow's 1842 "Aerial Steam Carriage". In 1847 they made a smaller craft on the same design, which would not fly.

COLL. BOB GARRET PHOTO: CHRIS BARKER

flights of 300 to 750 feet (90-230 m) in the 1890s, exercised control simply by moving his body, and only at the time of his death as the result of a flying accident in 1896, was engaged on the design of a body harness linked to a rear elevator on his latest glider.

During the second half of the 19th century a great effort went into achieving flight in England, France, the United States and Germany but it was diffused and fumbling. Little was known by one designer of what others were doing until Octave Chanute decided to collect and disseminate proved facts and other information to all who would listen to him. From 1896 onwards, he was engaged in building and flying his own gliders in the United States, and in spreading particulars about the principles involved in flight with fixed wings. In 1903 he visited Europe and lectured in Paris. Before that, he had given valuable help along the same lines to the Wright Brothers.

Some of these principles had been laid down by Cayley in 1809. He had outlined the forces of thrust, drag and lift, and had pointed out the value of the cambered, or arched, AEROFOIL wing shape in preference to the flat plate. As early as 1868, M P W Boulton in England had invented and patented the aileron. The Wrights' first glider of 1899 had wings that could be warped, or twisted, by cables for lateral control. Thus, by the time the Wrights made their first flight at the end of 1903, most of the devices for controlled flying were known and yet S P Langley in the United States and a string of pioneers in France and England were still meeting with little success. Even the Wrights in 1903 had not fully resolved the control situation; they found that wing-warping by itself was not enough. Their bright idea of linking the wing-warping with rudder movement was generously given away by Chanute to the Europeans, but too many of these still aimed at inherent stability through giving their wing tips a dihedral or upward-tilted angle.

There were many ambitious projects before real powered flight was accomplished by the Wrights. The biggest of them was the design by W S Henson in 1842 for an "Aerial Steam Carriage". It had a tail-piece to provide control and stability, box-kite wings, and a three-wheeled undercarriage for take off and landing. It was to have a span of 150 feet (46 m) with wings properly constructed using spars and ribs, and it was to be propelled by two six-bladed airscrews. It was never built. Hiram Maxim staged an elaborate experiment to prove lift in 1894 with a device that weighed $3\frac{1}{2}$ tons and applied 360 hp through two steam engines. It was not intended to fly but it did lift off its rails, and there the project ended. In 1895-6 the Englishman Pilcher, a disciple of Otto Lilienthal, made several successful glider flights on the banks of the Clyde. In France, people like du Temple de la Croix, Pénaud and Ader worked hard with model aeroplanes driven by steam, twisted rubber and clockwork. In England, H F Phillips came back to Cayley's cambered wing and further showed the distribution of pressure and lift between the upper and lower surfaces of a wing.

This incoherent jumble of effort was given fresh interpretation by the Wright Brothers. Having learned all they could about the research and development up to their time, they proceeded to put the most promising ideas to the test. At the same time, they worked out their own calculations

SCIENCE MUSEUM

200.000ᶠ de PRIX

GRANDE SEMAINE

D'AVIATION DE LA

REIMS DU 22 AU 29 AOÛT 1909 CHAMPAGNE

concerning not only the relation of thrust to lift and of the efficiency of propellers but also stresses and methods of construction. By their third glider they had developed a satisfactory airframe and began looking to the newly-arrived automobile engine for their power. Failing in their attempt to get from the new industry a petrol engine of a suitable power to weight ratio, they set to work to build their own engine; and on 17 December 1903 the first flight was made. Two months earlier S P Langley's latest aeroplane, also driven by a petrol engine and piloted by C M Manly, had fouled the launching mechanism and plunged into the Potomac. The triumph of Wilbur and Orville Wright was complete and exclusive. Orville, who made that first flight, was in the air only 12 seconds and travelled a distance of 120 feet (37 m). Three more flights were made that day and the last covered 852 feet (260 m). After that they went home to Dayton, Ohio from their flying ground at Kill Devil Hills in North Carolina and in 1904 built their second aeroplane, again a biplane, with reduced wing camber and a more powerful engine.

Little attention was paid to them and their achievements by the rest of the world but they continued their experiments in control and in 1905 they produced their third aeroplane. This was extremely successful and before the year ended, a flight of 24 miles (38 km) had been made at an average speed of 38 mph (61 km/h). For the next two and a half years, they did no flying. Futile negotiations with the US and British Governments and anxiety about the risk of having their secrets pried into were at the bottom of this inactivity. In 1908, Wilbur visited Europe in search of business while Orville stayed at home, preparing for the military trials to which the US authorities had at last consented.

Meanwhile, Europe had been moved to fresh effort by gliding pioneer Chanute's encouragement. In France this was led by Esnault-Pelterie, later to be a prominent figure, and yet the first copies of the Wright glider were failures. In England, S F Cody had worked forward from man-lifting kites to a relatively inefficient glider. Slightly earlier, in France, Léon Levavasseur had built a monoplane with birdlike wings. It was a failure but this pioneer together with that outstanding pioneer Louis BLERIOT were to give monoplanes a place in competition with the currently favoured biplanes.

The first aircraft factory was set up in 1905 at Billancourt, France, by the Voisin brothers, who had already built two float gliders towed by motor boats. They built for themselves and other designers, but the fashion in Europe was still to aim at stability rather than control. Soon the Brazilian pioneer aviator Santos-Dumont had turned away from airships to experiment with monoplanes and biplanes and also with tractor (front mounted) airscrews. In 1906, he flew 720 feet (220 m) in a tail first pusher biplane. In 1909, A V Roe in England produced a tractor biplane and J W Dunne built the world's first swept-wing aeroplane, again a biplane, and again aimed at inherent stability. A year later, F W Lanchester did for aerodynamics what Newton and Bernoulli had done for HYDRODYNAMICS, when he put forward his theory (never disputed) of the circulation of air over the wing surfaces.

By 1909, the Wrights had made flights in public on both sides of the Atlantic and the cause was given a healthy impetus. In the United States, Glenn Curtiss came to the fore as the designer of both aeroplane and engine in the June Bug, which had wingtip ailerons for lateral control. European designers, with the exception originally of Henri Farman, followed the Wrights in aiming at good control either by

Right: Bleriot's 1909 crossing of the English Channel was the first significant point to point flight. Although the journey was a meagre 23 miles (37 km), he only just made it across.

Below: Alcock and Brown's Vickers Vimy after their historic transatlantic flight of 1919. Their landing was less of a triumph than the flight itself, on account of the boggy nature of the ground where they landed in western Ireland.

Right: a Fokker DR1 triplane, one of the best known German aircraft of World War 1. This example is one of the few that survive in flying order.

Below: the Supermarine S.6B seaplane which won the Schneider Trophy in 1931. It later set a world speed record of 407 mph (655 km/h). It bears a strong family resemblance to the Spitfire, a later Supermarine design of 1936, and in fact was one of the most important influences on its design.

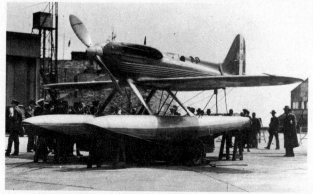

ALPHABET & IMAGE

Above: the World War 2 Supermarine Spitfire. For almost the entire war it was the fastest fighter in service, thanks to successive changes that increased its performance. This Spitfire XVI is a late model with square cut wingtips to reduce drag and a 'bubble' cockpit canopy. Below: the Douglas Dakota was of equal importance as a transport aircraft. Civilian versions remain in service today.

PHOTRI

wing-warping or by the fitting of ailerons. A string of new types now appeared and at the Rheims aviation week in August 1909, more than 30 aeroplanes were on show, six of them built to the Wright specification. A Curtiss successor to the June Bug won the speed contest at 47.85 mile/h (77 km/h) an Antoinette won the height award at 508 feet (155 m) and a Farman the distance at 112 miles (180 km). The same year Blériot had staggered across the English Channel in his underpowered monoplane and the aeroplane had ceased to be regarded as an erratic and essentially dangerous toy. Its progress was helped by the development of more powerful AERO ENGINES.

The Wright aeroplane types remained popular, but by 1910 the influence of the Wrights on development had virtually ceased and a vigorous independent line was being pursued by designers in various countries. The best performers continued to be biplanes though a good deal of work was done on monoplanes, and the germ of the cantilever wing, supported only by the fuselage instead of a system of wires, was contained in a patent registered by Junkers in Germany as early as 1910. A year later, another improvement appeared in a German device for raising the undercarriage legs on hinges to lie flush with the fuselage in flight. At the same time an oleo undercarriage leg (a telescopic leg incorporating an oil-filled shock absorber) was designed at the Royal Aircraft Factory at Farnborough, England. All these advances marked the movement from the wood-and-wire structure to the use of metal in aeroplanes. They also accompanied the increasing popularity of the tractor airscrew and the universal adoption of a tube shaped fuselage to connect the wings, tail and landing gear, and to provide a less exposed position for pilot, passengers and power plants.

The possible use of the aeroplane for military purposes had now become clear. The service view was that it might be made to serve reconnaissance purposes; but passengers had already been carried and other loads were obviously possible. Also the ability of the aeroplane to perform aerobatics had been demonstrated well before World War 1 broke out. Throughout that war, the aeroplane made great progress in Germany, France and England and the flimsy, underpowered box-kite aircraft were superseded by sturdier designs. Fokker came to the aid of Germany with a series of monoplanes which owed something to the Morane Parasol, a high wing design with the fuselage suspended beneath it, and something to the Junkers idea for a cantilever wing. England clung obstinately to biplanes and, after 1917, produced some remarkable efficient specimens not only in the single-seater field but also in the big bomber class. This distrust of the monoplane by the British persisted into the early thirties while Germany added to the cantilever wing the equally revolutionary method of stressed skin construction, which was also early adopted in the US. When England did at last come to monoplanes she had her own structural contribution to make, in the form of geodetic construction. This was a sort of open basketwork construction of aluminium strip so designed as to direct stresses to the surface and there distribute them over the whole surface. This was proved to be extremely resistant to war damage by the World War 2 Wellington bomber. Its disadvantage was that it could not compete in weight with the stressed skin method unless it used a fabric covering and this led to its disappearance as the stressed skin technique proved itself.

Progress in the 1920s The designs of the middle 1920s were not very different from those at the end of World War 1. Wire braced biplanes and monoplanes with external strut or wire bracing, both types powered usually by water cooled engines, continued to be popular. A prize of £25,000 had been offered in 1919 by an American, Raymond Orteig, for the first nonstop flight from Paris to New York. Charles Lindbergh, an American airmail pilot, finally won the prize in 1927. His Ryan monoplane, the Spirit of St Louis, flew 3600 miles nonstop in 33 hours and 39 minutes. From this point onwards air cooled engines were used extensively.

The last few years of the 1920s provided the impetus to explore more fully both the military and commercial aspects of flight. All the contests for endurance and speed records had brought modifications to aircraft design, but on a haphazard basis. New and reliable aircraft engines were being developed, which in turn led to improvements in other features in aircraft.

During this period, much work was done on other types of machine, such as the HELICOPTER, pioneered in the US by the Russian-born Sikorsky and in Germany by Focke and Achgelis. At the same time, the Spaniard Juan de la Cierva invented the AUTOGIRO, which has an unpowered rotor turned by the backwash from an ordinary airscrew.

Retractable landing gear was developed for use on amphibious aircraft by Loening and independently by Sikorsky but it was considered too costly and heavy for light aircraft. All this changed in the early 1930s when most aircraft were built with fold-up landing gear in the interests of more efficient air performance.

1930s developments

Apart from the acceptance of the necessity for retractable landing gear, wind tunnel studies produced new cross-sectional shapes for wings and other surfaces. These included the Handley Page automatic slot, an air-pressure operated device mounted on the leading edge of the wing to warn of an approaching stall, and also delay the actual stall by inducing an extra flow of air through the slot to smooth the air flow. At the trailing edge, movable flaps were attached to increase lift at low forward speeds by increasing the wing area and accentuating the camber of the wing.

New materials were tested and by the 1940s the wood, fabric and wire construction had almost disappeared. Most of the larger aircraft in the earlier 1930s were twin engine types and it was not until the end of the decade that four engine designs became usual. Aircraft such as the Boeing 247 of 1933 and the Douglas DC series of 1934 began to change the face of air transportation because they were fairly large and sound-proof and they carried enough electronic navigational and landing aids to make for safety in most weather conditions. For sea crossings large flying boats were developed by Latécoère of France. There were also Sikorsky's S-42 flying boat and later, flying clippers built by Glenn Martin and Boeing.

Designers in this period also began experimenting with the JET engine. The first flight of a jet aircraft was in August, 1939 by the German Heinkel He 178.

Development after 1940

World War 2 led to rapid advances in design. Although nearly all aircraft were still driven by piston engines, work on rocket and jet propulsion intensified. Almost two years after the first jet flight, in May 1941, the British Gloster aircraft powered by a Whittle jet engine took to the air. The US followed in October 1942 with their Bell XP 59A twin-jet aircraft. During World War 2 the Germans Busemann and Betz, and R T Jones in England worked on designs for SUPERSONIC FLIGHT, though this was finally achieved in the US by the Bell X-1 in 1947. By the end of World War 2 around 1300 Messerschmitt Me 262 twin jet fighters had been built and Britain was producing the Gloster F-9-40 Meteor.

Air transportation relied on propeller-driven aircraft until the emergence of the high speed jet powered designs which first appeared in the form of the de Havilland Comet in 1949. The hybrid turboprop engine, which uses jet power to drive a propeller, was invented later than the pure jet, but the first airliner to use it was built in 1948, just a year before the Comet. This was the British Vickers Viscount.

During the following years, the military importance of aircraft began to decline as they were superseded by various

Above: the prototype De Havilland Comet, the world's first jet airliner. This 1950 picture shows the original square cabin windows, which failed under pressure and caused a disastrous series of crashes. Below) the North American X-15, a rocket powered research aircraft. It is slung under the wing of a B-52 bomber and escorted by a Super Sabre 'pursuit' plane.

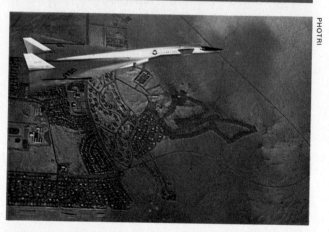

Above: the XB-70, a very large supersonic aircraft originally designed as a bomber. Changes in policy led to a greater dependence on missiles, however, and the prototypes were turned into 'flying laboratories' for research into high speed flight. They represent the ultimate point in aircraft design, beyond which progress is uneconomic.

types of missile. But civilian air travel became more and more important. This was reflected in the increasing size of airliners, culminating in the Boeing 747, which has a normal maximum capacity of about 450 passengers — though in practice most of them have their seats arranged to carry about two thirds of this number. Larger airliners are planned, with a capacity of 1000.

Supersonic airliners are also being built by the British, French and Russians. It will not be possible for some years to say whether they will be a commercial success. The design problems were solved some years before, but the main restraints on aircraft design are now economic rather than technical.

AIR CUSHION VEHICLE

Air cushion vehicles — also known as hovercraft or, in the United States of America, as ground effect machines (GEM) — are vehicles which when in motion are supported by a layer of air, rather than by wheels or other direct means of contact with the ground over which they pass.

This absence of contact with the surface has brought the advantages of both adaptability and speed: the latter is particularly well demonstrated when the ACV is compared with the conventional ship. For example, the large British passenger ACV, the 190-ton SR-N4, is capable of speeds of nearly 80 knots (150 km/h) and cruises at around 50 (90 km/h). The top speed for a crack liner is around 35 knots (65 km/h).

There are a number of reasons why this is so. First, in a conventional ship that area of the hull which is normally submerged is subjected to drag as a result of the VISCOSITY of the water through which it travels. Drag absorbs a good deal of engine power.

Second, wave formations are set up at bow and stern of a ship when it is under way. Again, this wave making process means a drain on the power supply. Although this is less important than drag at low speeds, as speed increases it takes over as the major power wastage problem.

Finally, there are the natural phenomena of currents and of windage on the exposed areas of hull and superstructure. These may sometimes work adversely.

Considering the first two factors alone, it can be appreciated that the bigger and faster the ship, the larger the amount of energy wasted. There comes a point when the cost of deriving more speed from a ship outweighs the advantages — unless there are special factors like military or research requirements.

Since none of the ACV is immersed it has none of these problems. At low speeds a wave making process is set up, but at cruising speeds this disappears. So though the ACV is affected by adverse winds, it is generally faster not only than a conventional vessel of the same size but also larger ships.

In principle the ACV works as follows. The hull can be thought of as being something like an upturned tea tray with raised edges. If such a structure were placed carefully on the surface of water, a quantity of air would be trapped beneath it, retained by the edges which would now be jutting downwards. If, however, you attempted to propel the tray through the water, the air would escape and the tray would sink. Even if that did not happen, the submerged portions of the edges would be subjected to friction and would set up waves.

The pioneer designers were faced with two problems: how to raise the craft clear of the water, and how to keep the air cushion permanently in place.

They overcame the first by ducting air into the cushion compartment at pressure a little higher than atmospheric, and the second by arranging a system of air jets around the edge to provide a curtain of air which slowed down the rate of leakage from the cushion. This system was improved by the addition of a flexible *skirt* around the edge of the vessel.

It has been calculated that a pressure of only about 60 lb per square foot (300 kg/m²) is required to raise an ACV of 100 tons or more to a height of one foot (30 cm). The pressure required to inflate car tyres is a good deal greater.

Types of ACV

Several variations of the basic ACV principle have been evolved. The simplest is called the *air-bearing* system. Air is blown through a central orifice in the undersurface and leaks away outwards under the flexible retaining skirt.

The *plenum chamber* vessel has a concave undersurface, and the cavity forms the upper section of a cushion chamber which is completed by the sea or ground surface. Again the air leaks away under the edges.

In the *momentum curtain* system a ring of air jets is set around the circumference of the underside of the ACV. The air from these jets is directed downwards and inwards to retain the air cushion. This system has been further developed to include two rows of peripheral jets, one inside the other. The retaining air is blown out through one set, sucked up by the other after it has done its job, and then recirculated. This makes for

Above: a number of these SR-N5 hovercraft were built for general purpose work. This one is seen on British Army-Navy duty in the Malayan jungle; others have been used on coastguard patrols on the western coast of Canada. They seat 18, or take 2 tons of freight. A larger version, the SR-N6, can take up to 56 passengers.

Left: a US Navy patrol air cushion vehicle leaves on a mission in the Mekong Delta.

JOHN BISHOP

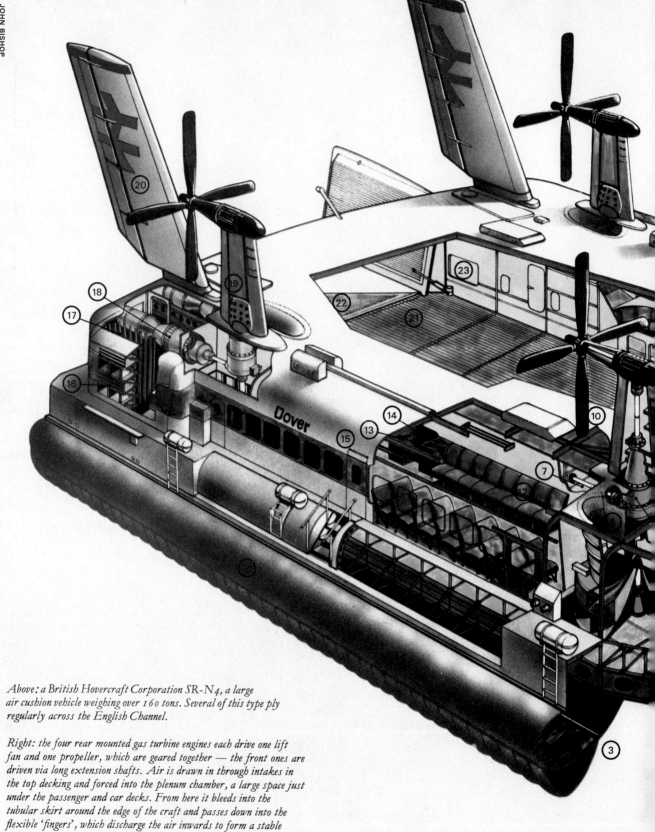

Above: a British Hovercraft Corporation SR-N4, a large air cushion vehicle weighing over 160 tons. Several of this type ply regularly across the English Channel.

Right: the four rear mounted gas turbine engines each drive one lift fan and one propeller, which are geared together — the front ones are driven via long extension shafts. Air is drawn in through intakes in the top decking and forced into the plenum chamber, a large space just under the passenger and car decks. From here it bleeds into the tubular skirt around the edge of the craft and passes down into the flexible 'fingers', which discharge the air inwards to form a stable air cushion. The fingers move up and down to follow the contours of the surface the craft is passing over, reducing air leakage.

1 forward car ramp
2 flexible skirt
3 skirt fingers
4 forward passenger compartment
5 12 blade lift fan
6 air intakes
7 extension shaft from turbine
8 main bevel drive gearbox
9 propellor gearbox
10 HS Dynamics propellor
11 air conditioning packs
12 main passenger compartment
13 baggage racks
14 door to car deck
15 passenger entrance door
16 engine intakes
17 acoustic baffles
18 Marine Proteus gas turbine
19 pylon
20 fin
21 car deck
22 rear car ramp
23 hatch to auxiliary power unit
24 crew entry ladder
25 control deck

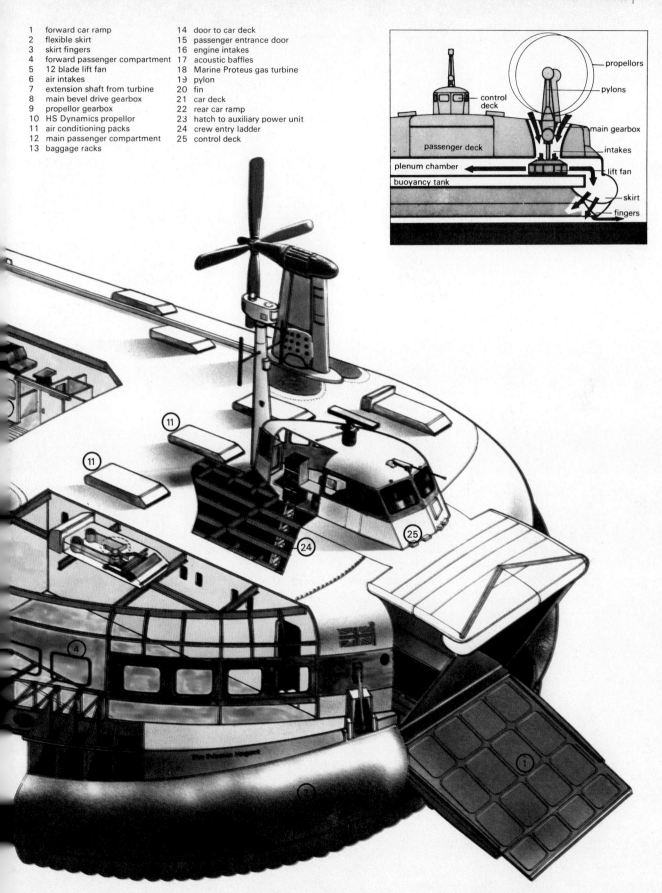

greater efficiency, since it slows down the rate of air escape.

ACV propulsion systems have also been varied. The most popular for large vessels has been the airscrew or propeller. In the earliest machines, the fans that provided lift also drove air through a system of ducts to the stern where it was ejected for propulsion. In the SR-N4, the four engines that drive the lift fans also drive external airscrews for propulsion. In many other types, however the lift and propulsion systems are separately powered. Some ACVs even have water propellers. These cannot go on land.

The problems of steering an ACV are very similar to those of steering an aeroplane. As the ACV has no contact with sea or land, there is a danger of drift during turns. The helmsman overcomes this by banking, or tilting, his machine like an aircraft. He does so by reducing the pressure from the air jets on the side which he wants to dip. Directional control is exerted by varying the power of the airscrew, by using aero rudders, or with both systems at once.

Development

The air cushion principle has fascinated designers for many years. Pioneering attempts at its use were made, for example, as far back as the 1930s, in both the United States and Finland. But it was not until after World War 2 that the real breakthrough came.

The inventor of the first successful ACV was Britain's C S Cockerell. Trained as an engineer and in electronics, he later turned his attention to the problems of boat design.

He tried at first to retain an air cushion under a boat by fitting hinged flaps at the bow and stern of his craft between side keels. Except for the hinging, it was almost exactly the same as the tea tray example.

Finding this technique to be ineffective, he replaced the flaps with sheets of water pumped vertically downwards. Air containment was still not very efficient, and finally he struck on the idea of using peripheral air jets for the purpose.

The world's first hovercraft, the SR-N1, was unveiled in 1959 when it travelled from the Isle of Wight to mainland England. Only a few weeks later it crossed the English Channel in two hours, and in 1965 the world's first regular passenger service was set up between the Isle of Wight and the mainland. Now a fleet of SR-N4s carries passengers and cars regularly to and from France, and in 1972 captured 29 per cent of the total traffic.

Uses of ACVs

The ACV has truly arrived as a means of providing high-speed transport over a variety of terrains.

Because the air cushion acts not only as a form of support but also as an effective spring, the modern ACV can cope with waves of up to ten feet (3 m) and can operate over rough ground as well. It has been used for military purposes by the US in Vietnam and elsewhere in the Far East. It was even employed on one occasion to carry a British expedition to the upper reaches of the Amazon.

The advantages of this type of craft in naval warfare are considerable. It is not only speedy, but the larger types can deliver torpedoes and other missiles with telling effect. At the same time, since they are not in contact with the sea themselves, they are immune to torpedo attack. The missile simply passes harmlessly beneath them.

But even that presupposes that an enemy submarine can find them. The insulation of the air cushion makes it impossible for submarine listening gear to pick up the sound of the ACV's propulsion system.

The United States Navy is developing a 2200 ton test craft, to be followed by a 10,000 ton version which will carry jet fighters of the vertical take off type.

For both civil and military purposes, the ACV has the advantage that it can make the transition from sea to shore with relative ease. No expensive docking facilities are required — just an area of gently shelving beach.

There is also the whole area of ACV application on dry land. The concept has been used in the design of several devices including a type of lawnmower, a 'hoverpallet' for transporting heavy loads around the factory, and enormous craft like the American ACT 375, designed to carry a 375-ton payload across the Arctic wastes. Work on 'hovertrains' is going on in the United States, France, Japan and the Soviet Union. The air cushion principle has even been applied to aircraft — the US Bell LA4 employs an air cushion instead of wheels for take off and landing.

AIRFOIL (see aerofoil)

The Voyageur ACV seen here was developed for use in Canada, where the wide variety of terrain, including lakes frozen in winter, makes it ideal. Its 25 ton capacity compares well with cargo aircraft.

AIR LOCK

The air lock is a chamber designed to allow movement between compartments containing air at different pressures, or between a pressurised or vacuum compartment and the outside atmosphere.

A very common application, and one which demonstrates the principle involved, is its use in the *caisson*. This device is used for carrying out work on submerged bridge foundations, harbour structures, and so on. It consists of a wide vertical tube which reaches from the surface to the work site.

To keep the tube free of water for the workers, the pressure of the air inside must be maintained at the same level as that of the water around its lower end — inevitably greater than the surface air pressure.

This could be achieved by simply sealing the top of the caisson with an airtight trap door and pumping air inside to the necessary pressure. However, as soon as anyone attempted to open the trap in order to enter or exit, the pressurised air inside would rush out. Water would then flood the caisson.

The problem is overcome by having two airtight trap doors with a space between — the air lock. If a workman wishes to leave, valves between the work area and air lock are opened, equalising the air pressures.

The workman can then climb the ladder to the lock and enter, closing the trap door and valves behind him to seal the work chamber again.

If he does not need to undergo DECOMPRESSION, the workman can open the upper door and let himself out. In this case, some of the high pressure air will rush out, but that in the work chamber will be unaffected.

If decompression is needed, then the pressure level in the lock is gradually reduced to atmospheric level by venting it through another set of valves in the upper door.

The journey is accomplished in reverse in very much the same way, except that the air in the lock will be at surface pressure when the workman enters. So, after the door is closed behind him the air pressure in the lock is pumped up until it is equal in pressure with the work chamber, allowing him to take the next step.

Similar air locks are employed in the construction of tunnels which run under the sea bed or under rivers. High pressure air is pumped into the work area to keep the water out, and pressure is maintained by a bulkhead. This air lock is of the walk-through variety, with an airtight door at each end, on either side of the bulkhead.

A further version of the air lock is used in submarines, either to allow the crew to escape in emergencies or to allow divers to work outside the hull. The difference here, though, is that the air pressure inside the submarine is always lower than that of the water outside. Hence, if exit were attempted simply by opening a hatch, the vessel would be rapidly flooded.

An air lock allows the departing diver to seal the first hatch behind him, thus rendering the submarine safe, and then to open the valves on the outer door to let the sea water in. When the lock is filled with water, he can open the outer door and leave.

On re-entry, he shuts the outer door, blows out the sea water with compressed air, and closes the outer valves. Then he equalises pressure with that inside the sumbarine at a speed necessary to prevent decompression sickness, and enters the main hull area.

Similar air lock systems are used to allow divers to be transferred from undersea habitats to surface vessels; to allow astronauts to venture from their spacecraft into the vacuum of space; and to allow workers to move in and out of certain areas of nuclear reactors which have contaminated air. They are also needed occasionally for other uses; an unusual type of lock, shown on this page, is used to insert materials in a furnace that has to be kept at a high vacuum.

FIRTH BROWN LTD.

Above: an airlock on a vacuum remelting furnace, which melts metals to make alloys away from the oxidizing effect of the air.
Below: how it works. A wagonload of metal approaches the outer door (1) which is opened to let it into the lock (2). The pump exhausts the air from the lock (3) before the inner door is opened (4).

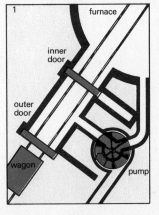
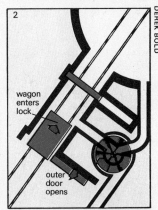
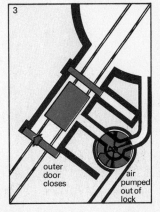
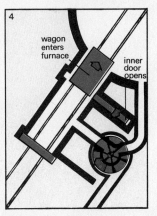

DEREK BOLD

AIRPORT

At one time, airports were located in convenient fields as close as possible to the city they were to serve, without much regard to environmental problems. It was difficult in those days to envisage the growth potential of civil aviation and the complexity of air services and airports to handle them. Today, the spread of cities and the greater importance of air travel mean that airports have to be planned to meet a careful balance of aviation and environmental needs.

A major airport requires a good highway and rail links with the city centre. Passengers should be able to park their cars within a short walk of the berth in which their airliner is docked. They do not want to have to park a long, confusing walk away, struggling with baggage through rain, traffic and disembarking passengers to the terminal building.

In between the car and the airliner, the airport, airlines and control authorities like immigration and customs must provide the embarking passenger with, in order: ticket and check-in counters, passport checkpoints for international flights, concourses with lounge and general consumer services such as duty-free shops and a pier connecting the terminal with the door of the aircraft. The disembarking passenger wants to get out of the airliner as quickly as possible and either leave the airport or get to another berth to catch a connecting airliner. If he is catching a connecting flight he wants to get to the appropriate berth — though it might be literally miles away — without a long walk and without bothering about his baggage. All this has to be accomplished without mixing inward and outward bound passengers.

Passengers who choose to go to and from the airport by

rail have similar requirements. Ideally, their train should serve all the berths on the airport without requiring passengers to change. Another track should be used for automated shuttle services between airliner berths.

To these passengers' requirements the airport designer must now add those of the airlines. An airport like London's Heathrow employs about 50,000 people whose jobs include dealing with passengers and their baggage, servicing and refuelling aircraft, air traffic control and so on. Nearly as many workers may go into and out of an airport each day as passengers. They want car parks and offices, and separate access for service vehicles to the airliners.

The aircraft themselves make great demands on space. Runways 12,000 feet (3.7 km) long and 150 feet (45 m) wide are required for modern commercial jets. Ideally there should

be at least two runways, each aligned with the prevailing wind and with turn-offs and taxiways for the least taxying time to and from the terminal.

A modern airliner berth requires a terminal frontage of at least 300 feet (90 m). During rush hours at big airports there may be as many as 50 airliners in dock. This represents a frontage of some three miles. If each airliner has 350 seats it may generate a hundred cars; half a dozen airliners a day may dock in that berth and so parking for 600 cars has to be found near each berth.

The aircraft also need parking and maintenance space. Planes these days are designed for 'on-condition' or 'on-wing' maintenance, in which replacements for faulty units are simply fitted while the plane is parked.

Airliners have to be 'turned round' as quickly as possible

Far left: an aerial view of New York's John F Kennedy airport. Nearly all the central space is devoted to car parking. This area is surrounded by a hollow ring of airport buildings, then by parking and taxying space for aircraft, then by the runways. The inner area is reached by a tunnel visible at the top (north) corner. The famous curving shells of Eero Saarinen's TWA terminal can be seen at the right.

Above left: the air terminal, sited in a town centre, relieves some of the strain on an airport by allowing passengers to check in before they reach it. This one is in Frankfurt.

Above right: security checking is becoming more important and thorough every year. Here a man runs the gauntlet of a metal detector at Copenhagen.

Centre left: the lighting of a modern airport is immensely complicated and stretches for miles from the runway. It must be maintained with great care.

Centre right: a night scene at Cologne airport. Routine maintenance of aircraft continues day and night. Every hour spent on the ground loses money.

Bottom: in spite of all these precautions, accidents happen. When they do, the important thing is to get to the scene quickly and take action immediately before the highly flammable jet fuel starts an uncontrollably large fire.

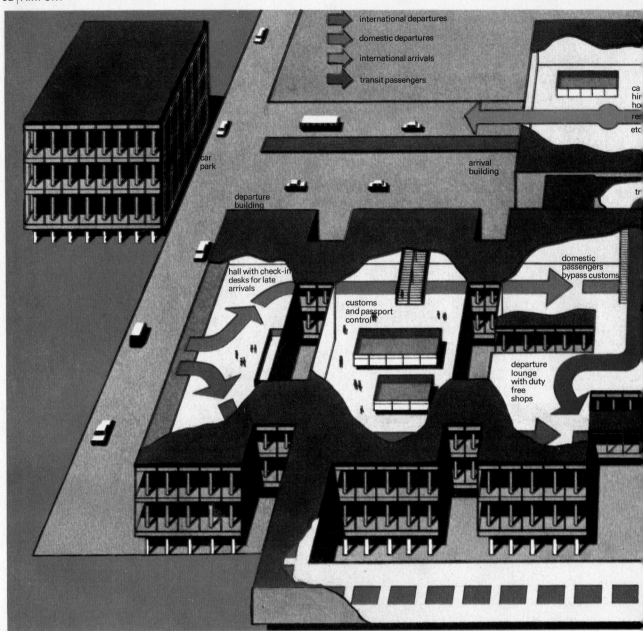

international departures
domestic departures
international arrivals
transit passengers

car park

arrival building

departure building

ca hir ho res etc

hall with check-in desks for late arrivals

customs and passport control

domestic passengers bypass customs

departure lounge with duty free shops

Above: a simplified schematic diagram of a modern airport. Routes through the building have to be carefully organized so that streams of passengers going in different directions do not mix, which would cause confusion and allow the dishonest to dodge ticket and passport checks. Each passenger must be passed through the appropriate stages one by one in the right order, but the layout must be flexible enough to allow for other arrangements if part of the airport has to be closed, for example during rebuilding. The main requirement is plenty of space, but this creates its own problems by forcing passengers to travel great distances from one part of the building to another. Escalators and 'travelators' — horizontal passenger conveyors — are helping with this problem in the newer airports.

Left: airports were not always so well organized. This 1946 picture shows the passenger reception tents at London Heathrow not long after it was opened. These primitive facilities were more or less all the passengers had at first, but since then the airport has never stopped growing and is now one of the largest and busiest in the world.

baggage jetty

arriving aircraft

customs and passport control

passenger jetty

...gers go straight to departure lounge

to domestic flight

passenger jetty

departing aircraft

baggage jetty

between flights to reduce costly time spent on the ground, when they are not actively earning money. The time between flights may be as little as twenty minutes, during which passengers have to be disembarked, the aircraft refuelled, maintained, cleaned and re-provisioned and the next lot of passengers embarked. These activities have to be carefully scheduled to avoid clashes, or the fire risk of passengers embarking during refuelling.

Finally, the design has to allow for the rapid growth of air transport, permitting terminals to be added or extended without the 'alterations as usual during business' that characterize so many airports.

The airliner approaches to land by ILS (Instrument Landing System). ILS equipment on the ground provides the approaching airliner with heading (directional) and glidepath information (see AVIONICS). Aircraft normally join the centre line (align themselves with the runway) at about five to seven miles (8 to 11 km) from the runway and follow the guidance

beams until the aircraft is landed. The procedures are becoming increasingly automatic and many of the latest aircraft can carry out the complete approach and landing without any manual pilot control at all. This does require airport landing aids of the most modern type.

ILS was originally designed for use in bad weather, but is now regularly used at major airports to keep traffic flowing (see AIR TRAFFIC CONTROL).

RADAR is a valuable partner for ILS. Surveillance radar normally covers several hundred square miles of airspace around each airport. An incoming airliner is seen as a 'blip' on the radar screen, which is used by the air traffic controller to steer the pilot on to the ILS beam.

Less busy airports use VOR (VHF Omni Range) beacons, which are also used as en route radio beacons. As an approach aid VOR is less satisfactory than ILS because it gives heading guidance only.

Visual landing aids are still important. The visual approach slope indicator, or VASI, which operates day and night, is not a substitute for ILS, being an 'airfield-in-sight' aid. Bars of red and white lights on either side of the runway are angled to show the pilot all red lights when he is below the glidepath, red and white lights when he is on the correct glidepath, and all white when he is too high. These lights are on either side of the touchdown point of the runway.

The approach to the runway is indicated by Calvert approach lighting with a white centre line crossed by five white bars, getting narrower as the runway approaches.

The runway itself has white centreline lights and bars to mark the touchdown area. At the end of the runway, the centreline becomes all red. The edges of the runway are marked with white lights. The latest design taxiways have green centreline lighting, replacing the blue edge lights that were formerly used.

The lights set into the runway are carefully designed to withstand the 300 tons or so exerted by a landing aircraft, and yet present no obstacle. The light from a 200 W tungsten-halogen bulb shines through an aperture no more than ½ inch (13 mm) high.

Runways have to be kept clear of foreign objects — stones, parts of aircraft, and so on. The danger of a burst tyre requires a considerable investment in runway vacuum cleaners and sweepers. These work throughout the hours of operations.

In snow clearance the trend is towards motorized trains incorporating plough-blade, brush and blower. The level of investment depends upon snow statistics and runway area. It is particularly difficult to judge in countries such as those of northern Europe, where snow may come as light powder one year and 6 feet (2 m) deep the next.

Without doubt the airport's least used equipment is its fire, crash and rescue vehicles. The introduction of larger aircraft has required big increases in the quantities of fire-extinguishing materials, such as foam, that can be produced. The trend is towards a 'knock-out punch' — a large quantity of material applied in one minute so that people can be got out.

A fleet of 'Quick Dash Trucks' carrying cutting devices, breathing apparatus, ladders, axes and other rescue equipment is on constant alert to be first on the scene of an accident.

More commonly seen on the tarmac of an airport are aircraft tugs. Tugs capable of pulling and pushing aircraft of up to 750 tons are now in prospect. Another familiar sight is the fuel bowsers, which can carry up to 20,000 Imperial gallons (90,000 litres). A Boeing 747 has a capacity for twice this amount, so large airports are installing hydrants linked by underground piping to a 'fuel farm' storage centre. With this system, flow rates of 500 gallons/minute (2250 litres/minute) are possible and flows of double this are envisaged.

The airport provides the space, and the airline supplies the equipment, for cargo landing. The standard international pallets and CONTAINERS are nowadays common to the biggest and smallest airports. The transfer between aircraft hold and surface vehicle is dealt with by equipment ranging from the simple roller-slide or fork-lift truck to automatic power conveyors. The scissor- or direct-lift platform lends itself well to big and heavy loads and high holds, and is standard equipment — truck or trailer mounted — wherever cargo has to be offered up to aircraft of different hold heights. Aircraft victualling containers, for example, are frequently scissor-lifted to the aircraft galley door.

The economic facts of life are that whoever provides all these airport facilities will seek to cover his costs and make a reasonable commercial return on his investment through landing fees and ancillary income like car parks, duty-free shops, catering etc. The passenger ultimately pays through the price of his ticket and his use of the facilities.

A night view of Heathrow airport, showing the lines of aircraft berths connected by passenger jetties.

AIRSHIP

While an AIRCRAFT obtains its lift from its speed through the air and the AEROFOIL wing shape, the airship or *dirigible* uses a gas which is lighter than air. The forward motion is provided by motor-driven propellers.

The gas in the gasbag is considerably lighter than the air it displaces, thus making the airship as a whole slightly lighter than its own volume of air. It therefore rises until it has reached a height where the air is thinner, and so light enough to balance the airship.

This lift has to be controlled to make an airship workable. Early airships used to do this by releasing gas and replacing it with air, a wasteful method that caused a gradual reduction of lift as more and more gas was lost. This could be compensated for by carrying water ballast, which could be released to lighten the airship. But later airships replaced the system with *ballonets*, collapsible air bags inside the gasbag but connected to the outside air. By varying the amount of air in these with pumps, the volume of the gas in the rest of the bag can be changed. There are usually two ballonets, to the forward and rear of the gasbag, so that the balance of the ship can be adjusted.

The tailfins operate just like those on an aircraft, and are the control surfaces by which the ship is steered. Conventional elevators are used to change the altitude of the craft when it is moving; the change of atmospheric pressure with altitude is compensated for automatically by varying the amount of air in the ballonets.

The lightest gas is hydrogen, which is comparatively cheap to manufacture. But its extreme flammability has resulted in the much more expensive, slightly less effective, but completely safe helium being used in all modern airships. Helium is found in small amounts with natural gas in the United States, but is otherwise very expensive to produce in large quantities.

Types of airship

There are, or have been, three categories of airship, *rigid, semi-rigid* and *non-rigid*. The rigid types consisted of a light metal framework containing several gasbags slung inside under nets, and with a separate outer cover. The German Zeppelins and most airships of the 1920s and 1930s were this type. The metals used were aluminium alloys, the outer skin was of cotton, and the gasbags were cotton lined with 'goldbeater's skin', a thin membrane taken from the intestines of cows.

The other types, semi-rigid and non-rigid, are known together as pressure airships since their shape is maintained mostly by the internal pressure. The semi-rigid types had a metal keel along the length of the envelope. The Norge, an Italian airship which flew from Rome to Alaska over the North Pole in 1926 was a semi-rigid craft.

The only type still used today is the non-rigid or *blimp*, which has no internal framework. Modern airships are made in this way of a synthetic fibre, Dacron, coated with neoprene, a man-made rubber. Aluminium paint on the outside reflects the sun's light and heat, reducing the extent to which the interior is heated. Battens on the nose prevent the wind pressure from flattening it when the craft is moving.

Development

In the beginning it was France that led the way. After the invention of the BALLOON in 1783, ways were sought of making it independent of the direction of the wind. The problem was to produce a suitable light yet powerful means of propulsion, and it was Henri Giffard who first produced a 3 hp engine weighing 350 lb (160 kg). His 70,500 cu ft (2000 m^3) hydrogen-filled craft ascended from the Hippodrome in Paris in 1852, and flew at 6 mile/h (9 km/h).

There was an improvement on this in 1884 when the French built another airship, La France, of about the same capacity. This was given a top speed of 15 mile/h (24 km/h) by the use of a 9 hp electric motor.

Germany came into the picture in 1895 with the first rigid

Above: the skeleton of a rigid airship is a light alloy lattice braced with wire. Lightness is vital, or the airship will not have a useful payload. Here the 1917 British airship No. 23 is being weighed with spring balances (white discs) to check that it does not exceed its designed weight.

Left: May 6 1937—the giant 'Hindenburg' burns at Lakehurst, New Jersey.

rigid airship

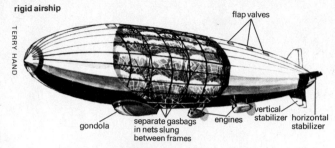

flap valves

gondola — separate gasbags in nets slung between frames — engines — vertical stabilizer — horizontal stabilizer

blimp

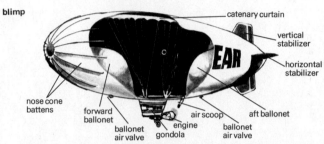

catenary curtain

vertical stabilizer

horizontal stabilizer

nose cone battens — forward ballonet — ballonet air valve — engine — gondola — air scoop — ballonet air valve — aft ballonet

Above: comparison of a rigid airship and a blimp. Inside its metal frame the rigid had several separate gasbags supported by nets. These were normally filled with hydrogen, which was vented through flap valves at the top to allow the airship to descend. The modern blimp is filled with helium, which is too expensive to vent. Instead it has internal ballonets into which air is pumped to compress the helium (making it heavier) as well as bringing the blimp down by its own weight. To make it ascend, the air is vented through valves.

Below: two views of the 'Europa', one of the four Goodyear blimps which are the only airships in existence today.

airship, built by David Schwarz. It was braced internally by a system of steel wires. Five years later, Count Zeppelin carried this idea further in his much bigger airship, built at Friedrichshafen. This had an aluminium frame consisting of 16 hoops connected and kept rigid by wire stays longitudinally and diagonally. The design proved a success and although one was lost, more than 20 airships of the same type were built. On the power of two 15 hp Daimler engines, it made a speed of about 26 mile/h (42 km/h). In 1912, the latest of this class carried 23 passengers on a cruise of seven and a half hours. The Germans were thus well prepared to use airships for military purposes when war broke out in 1914.

In contrast, the British had given only spasmodic attention to the development of the airship. A start on a programme had been made in 1902 but work petered out when the money was exhausted. In 1907 the Nulli Secundus was flown around London and in 1910, the small Beta made 330 flights. The first British rigid appeared in 1911, the Mayfly of 660,000 cu ft (18,700 m³) fitted with two 200 hp engines. She broke her back on her first flight and the British airship project came to an end. Thus at the Battle of Jutland, the British fleet had no airborne observers whereas the German fleet had the help of 29 airships. Soon the Zeppelins were making raids on English targets. These caused much anxiety but the lack of air observation was found most ominous in the anti-submarine war. As a result, the Royal Navy arranged for the construction of some small, non-rigid airships, which proved excellent at detecting and attacking enemy submarines. The British finished the war in 1918 with a fleet of 103; Germany had 68 rigids.

A fresh move was made by the British in 1918 through the purchase from Italy of a semi-rigid airship. This gave rise to a class of semi-rigids in the next few years. In the same period, the US made an arrangement with the Zeppelin company out of which came the ZR1, called the Shenandoah, which used helium instead of hydrogen. After 57 flights, she was lost in a thunderstorm. The US persisted in development work and, apart from building the Akron and the Macon, both of 6 million cu ft (170,000 m³) capacity, invented a metal skin for small airships. The first of these ships, the Metalclad, of 200,000 cu ft (5700 m³), did five years' work mostly in training crews. Its metal skin consisted of panels joined together by a riveting machine that used wire as rivets.

The heyday of the giant rigid airships was in the late 20s and the 30s. The US decided to use only helium in its airships, and banned its export. This meant that the large British and German craft had to rely upon hydrogen. The flammability of the gas and the lack of manoeuvrability of the ships often had appalling consequences. Many of the largest airships met with disaster, notably the British R101 in 1930, the American Akron and Macon in 1933 and 1935, and the Zeppelin Hindenburg in 1937.

The heavy losses of life in these crashes swung opinion against the use of airships, and they were no longer used for carrying passengers. But later, during the Second World War, the US used large numbers of non-rigid airships without a single loss for sea patrolling. Their ability to operate for long periods of time at low speed and low altitude made them invaluable for detecting minefields and escorting convoys.

More recently, Goodyear have built four non-rigid airships, which are often used as vibration free airborne platforms for television sports coverage.

Modern advocates of airships have suggested that they could be used profitably for cargo operation.

AIR TRAFFIC CONTROL

Air traffic control, ATC, is one of the most vital factors in air safety. It is a system for preventing collisions between aircraft in congested areas, particularly in the neighbourhood of airports, where the air is full of aircraft of different sizes travelling in various directions at various speeds and heights. ATC also keeps air traffic flowing smoothly.

On those parts of long distance routes which are uncongested, the pilot uses the built in navigational aids of his aircraft, and sometimes electronic aids on the ground, to make his own way and avoid collisions without help. But as soon as he approaches a much flown over area, or nears an airport, he enters a control zone, where he is obliged to follow a course at a given speed and height, all prescribed to him by the air traffic controller.

The air traffic controller is the decision maker. It is he alone who has complete information on all aircraft movements within his control zone. He must exercise powers of discretion on the minimum safe spacing between aircraft, both vertically and horizontally, and determine priority in take-off and landing within the framework of flight schedules.

The minimum information required by a controller is the current height and position of all aircraft under his control, the intentions of all aircraft under, or soon to be under, control, and the identity of each aircraft. He gets this information from a *flight progress board* which tells him intention, identification, vertical position and timing, and from a *plan position radar* which gives the exact position and distance of all aircraft within his control zone.

The controller's work involves continuous updating of information as new situations develop and earlier ones pass from his control. He receives advance information of traffic about to enter his control zone from adjacent zones and informs adjacent zones of traffic leaving his zone. He also monitors and controls all traffic within his zone.

The controller communicates with the aircraft normally by VHF (very high frequency) radiotelephone with a range of up to 200 miles (300 km) when the aircraft is at high altitude although the range decreases as the aircraft descends. A *radio direction finder* (RDF) system is frequently employed with the VHF radio link to supply compass bearing of any call received.

ARCHIBALD MCLEAN

ARCHIBALD MCLEAN

Left: two views of the inside of the control tower at Chicago's O'Hare airport, one of the largest, busiest and most modern airports in the world. The sheer number of aircraft on the ground and in the air, and the amount of data about them that has to be taken in, combine to make the air traffic controller's job uniquely demanding. Although he is backed up by radar and computer, in the final analysis it is his judgement that ensures the safety of every aircraft.

Wind speed and direction, visibility, cloud base, air temperature and barometric pressure data is fed to the controller from local sources and from meteorological centres. Runway visibility can now be accurately measured by electronic means rather than by someone's personal estimate, as is still usual today.

Flight plans

With certain exceptions, each flight requires a *flight plan* which includes aircraft identification, airport of departure and destination, .route plan, desired cruising level, departure time and estimated time of arrival. The data is transmitted, generally by land line rather than radio, to the ATC control centre from airports within the controller's zone or from adajcent zones. The information is always to a standard format.

Radar control systems

The basic RADAR system gives a continuous plan, as seen from above, of all aircraft within radar range. The *plan position indicator* (PPI) radar display shows an aircraft 'target' as a bright spot with the range (distance) of the aircraft indicated by its distance from the centre of the screen and its bearing by the angle to the centre. An electronic means known as video mapping makes it possible to permanently superimpose fixed features such as defined airways on the screen. It is also possible to eliminate all unwanted permanent radar echoes from stationary objects and display only those which are actually moving (moving target indicators).

In yet another refinement the radar echo from a particular aircraft can be 'tagged' with its identity or other information as a code of letters and numbers, the identity tag slowly moving across the screen in synchronization with the movement of the aircraft.

PPI type radars are in three broad categories, long range surveillance, airfield control and airfield surface movement. *Long range surveillance* radars have typically up to 300 nautical miles (550 km) range from power of the order of two megawatts peak power. *Airfield control* radars operating at less power have typically 50 to 150 nautical miles (95 to 280 km) range. *Airfield surface movement* radars are designed for very high definition and range is normally confined to runways, taxi-ways and aprons of the immediate .airfield. Modern surface movement radars have sufficient picture resolution to identify individual aircraft types by their shape and size.

These radars are all of the 'primary' type, which obtain information from a reflection of the radar beam from the

Below: VASI (visual approach slope indicator) is a simple but effective means of keeping an incoming pilot on the right glidepath as he nears the runway. It consists of two sets of lights fitted with reflectors and slats so that they send out red light over a very narrow angle and white light over an equally narrow, but higher, angle. They are carefully aligned so that if the pilot approaches at the right slope he will see one red and one white light on each side. If he is too high he will see all white lights, if too low, all red.

Right: a complete picture of London's Heathrow airport shown by the airfield surface movement radar. Individual aircraft are clearly visible, their long 'shadows' radiating outwards from the central aerial on the control tower. The map of the same area (opposite page) shows how close the picture is to reality. It is used with the radar picture to segregate aircraft and prevent collisions on the ground.

ERIC JEWELL ASSOC

too high   correct height   too low

aircraft or other 'targets', and require no co-operation from the aircraft. Another important type of radar system is known as *secondary surveillance radar* (SSR) in which equipment carried on the aircraft receives the transmitted ground signal and transmits a reply. The reply is entirely automatic and generally includes a coded message giving identity of the aircraft and present altitude, both of which can be integrated into the main PPI display and 'tagged' to the appropriate aircraft on the display. The airborne equipment of the SSR is called a *transponder,* because it responds to a received signal by transmitting another signal.

Instrument landing system The controller normally controls aircraft up to the final approach to the airfield when the pilots can lock on to the *instrument landing system* (ILS). This system provides a fixed radio beam so that an aircraft can align itself with the runway and adopt the correct descent path. The equipment comprises two ground transmitters, one emitting a beam to guide the aircraft in *azimuth* or compass bearing, the other a beam to guide the aircraft in altitude. The beams are known respectively as the *localizer* and *glidepath*. Both beams are modulated with tones at audio frequency (at a pitch which enables them to be heard) which are used to activate instruments in the aircraft flight deck (or indicate audibly to the pilot) whether he is deviating to the left or right of the centre line and above or below the glidepath.

Along the approach centre line are three vertically transmitted fan shaped beams known as the outer, middle, and inner *marker beacons*. Once brought to the position for final approach, the marker beacons indicate the distance to go, and the ILS system proper shows any deviation from the centre line and glidepath. If he keeps to the centre line and glidepath he will be brought accurately to the threshold of the runway at about 200 ft (60 m) altitude and can then complete the landing visually. The controller directs the aircraft to the appropriate runway exit for parking and discharge of passengers.

Blind landing Suitably equipped aircraft can use ground based ILS (provided it is of exceptional accuracy) combined with the autopilot and additional airborne electronic aids (principally highly accurate radar ALTIMETERS) to land in near zero visibility. The main complexity in such a system is the duplication and even triplication of airborne equipment to secure acceptable reliability.

Blind landing has been achieved thousands of times in

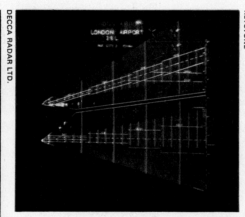

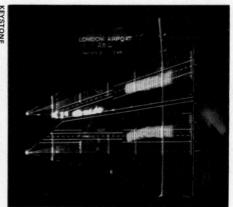

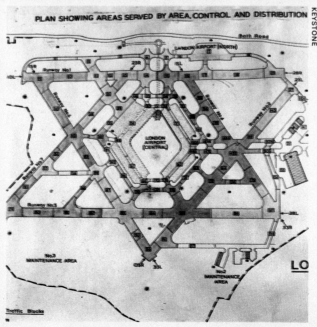

Above: aircraft without on-board landing aids must be monitored by Precision Approach radar. This enables the controller to keep an eye on the exact path taken by a landing aircraft from ten miles (16 km) out (left-hand screen) and in greater detail from three miles (5 km) out (right-hand screen). In each case the upper picture maps the plane's angle of descent and the lower one its alignment with the runway. The path of the aircraft is shown as a moving dot, here lengthened into a blur by a ten-second time exposure to make it more visible. The path that the aircraft should be on is shown by a dotted line. The plane on the left screen is too low and too far to the right; the other one is more or less in line.

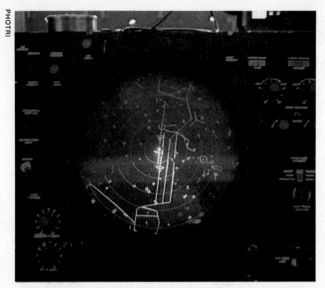

Above: the screen of a PPI (plan position indicator) radar used to survey aircraft movements near an airfield. This set uses 'video mapping' to superimpose a map of the surroundings on the radar picture, allowing the 'blips' that represent aircraft to be seen in their true position above features on the ground.

commercial practice but always in acceptable visibility as part of the proving trials. The pilot has the system engaged but monitors the landing throughout and is ready to take manual control at any instant. Completely blind landing will become a reality when the equipment is fully proved.

A parallel development is the provision of blind guidance for surface vehicles such as fire appliances and ambulances in case of accident in zero visibility conditions.

Stacking

At times of great congestion it is necessary for aircraft to queue, awaiting instructions to land. The controller directs aircraft to a holding or stacking area where aircraft fly round and round one above the other but separated by a safe vertical distance of about 1000 ft (300 m). The lowest aircraft is called off first after which the remaining aircraft descend one stage lower according to the safe stacking separation height. Aircraft arriving at a stacking area take the uppermost position.

Modern aids

The electronic COMPUTER now plays a central role in ATC in information processing and storage and supplying data to individual controllers in a large complex. Its main function is to reduce the workload on controllers so that they can concentrate on supervision of aircraft movements and decision making.

The Eurocontrol Maastricht Automatic Data Processing system (MADAP), which became fully operational in 1975, is a good example of a modern ATC system as it is multinational in the equipment used, the ATC officers who work in it, the countries that support it and the aircraft which fly through its area of operation.

MADAP now controls the upper air space of a region covering Belgium, Luxemburg, the Netherlands and the northern part of the Federal Republic of Germany. Its design incorporates all the features outlined above with the exception of ILS and other ground aids which do not apply to upper air space.

The ATC centre receives data from four radar centres and a continuous stream of flight data from airports and adjoining areas. All inputs, including radar data, are then processed through high power computers to provide controllers with the information they want as soon as it is needed. For example, the incoming flight plans are held in the computer store until the aircraft concerned are entering the area. The computer complex also performs such tasks as printing out events such as an aircraft passing over a reporting point as they occur, and predicts conflict conditions. But automation is kept firmly in place. The equipment is only there to aid the controller, who is still the final decision maker.

The MADAP installation has eight computers, more than 80 operating and training positions for controllers and some 140 radar and data display units. It is designed to deal simultaneously with 200 flight plans and 250 aircraft tracks.

Below: ILS (instrument landing system) uses narrow radio beams to guide aircraft down to land. Four beams are transmitted upwards: the stacking beam, around which planes circle as they wait to land, and the outer, middle and boundary markers to tell the pilot how far he has gone. Two other beams are angled slightly upwards at 3°-4° towards the aircraft: one, the localizer beam, is horizontally polarized; the other, the glide path beam, vertically. Their crossing marks the correct line of approach. A clearance antenna wipes out unwanted parts of the beam.

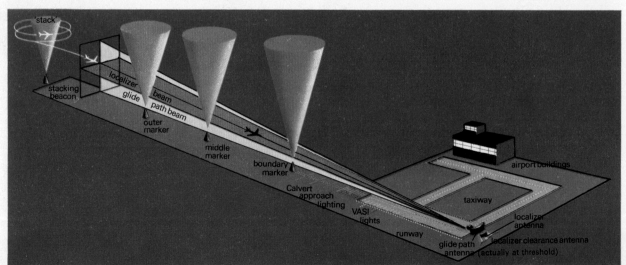

ALCHEMY

Alchemy was a pseudo-science concerned with changing base metals into GOLD and finding an elixir to prolong life indefinitely. It flourished from the first century AD to the seventeenth century attracting the attention of metalworkers, churchmen, doctors, kings and emperors. Unfortunately, a number of charlatans bent on making a quick fortune also practised it. Otherwise it was a respected occupation, the first system of organized experiment, and not, as many suppose, steeped in magic.

Alchemy developed at the same time as early chemical technology. The two interacted but it must not be thought that alchemy was the forerunner of modern CHEMISTRY. It was only one of its tributaries.

The word alchemy itself may have been derived from the Greek word *chyma* meaning the fusing or casting of metal, or it may be from the name for Ancient Egypt, *Chem* or black land. The prefix *al* was added during its Arab revival in the Dark Ages.

The origins of alchemy

The origins of alchemy are obscure but it became established between 100 and 300 AD during the Hellenistic (Greek) occupation of Alexandria in Egypt. It evolved from a combination of Greek philosophy, Egyptian technology and Middle Eastern astrology. Later, as Hellenistic philosophy embraced the doctrines of Gnosticism, Neoplatonism and Christianity, mystical influence became stronger.

Arts such as metalworking, DYEING, the preparation of drugs and COSMETICS were well known to the Egyptians and many of the techniques used contributed to alchemical practice. The first chemists were metallurgists used to working with gold and silver for their wealthy patrons and, in turn, producing cheaper substances for the poorer citizens. Naturally, they were interested in turning cheaper materials into what looked like gold. The effects they produced interested philosophers.

From Greek philosophy came Aristotle's theory (*c* 350 BC) that four fundamental forms or qualities could be ascribed to all matter — hot, dry, wet and cold. These in turn gave rise to four elements: fire, earth, air and water, of which all matter was made up in varying proportions. But to round this theory off there was one ultimate matter, *prima materia,* from which everything was formed. Nature was constantly striving to perfection so all matter was undergoing changes towards this goal. Later this *prima materia* became known as the *quinta essentia* or spirit. It was a fifth quality superior to the four elements and was believed to exist in all bodies and was capable of being distilled out.

METALS were thought to grow and undergo changes like man and could therefore be killed off prematurely and revived in a more perfect form. COPPER, for example, could be 'killed' by converting it to copper oxide, which blackens it, and then treated with arsenic to 'revive' it to a silver-coloured and therefore more perfect alloy. Other reagents produced different colour changes and presented various stages towards the ultimate perfection in metal, gold. Colours played an important part in the theory and the correct order of change was considered to be from black to white to yellow to red. The alchemists believed that one powerful transmuting agent must exist which would not only bring metals to a state of perfection but also prolong man's life. This unknown substance was called *aliksir* (elixir) by the Arabs while European alchemists named it the 'philosopher's stone' or

Above: a 15th century alchemist and his assistants at work. The balance in a glass case is very unusual because changes in weight were not important in alchemy.

Above: a popular belief among alchemists was that all metals were made from mercury and sulphur combined in different proportions. This picture symbolizes the union of sulphur (red) and mercury (green).

the 'tincture'. In spite of names which appear to be associated with some form of liquid or stone, the alchemists usually thought of it as a stable, heavy red powder. Later, the famous Arabian alchemist Jabir, or his followers, decided that all metals were composed of mercury and sulphur and if these elements were pure and in equilibrium the product would be the perfect metal, gold.

The development of alchemy

The development of alchemy can be traced through texts and books, although for the first thousand years or so only one or two major works survived and even then their authenticity is sometimes in doubt. It was the practice to ascribe written works to some god, hero, king or philosopher such as Moses, Hermes, Cheops or Cleopatra. Notable early writers on alchemy were a Democritus who wrote '*Physica and Mystica*', and Zosimus of Panopolis who wrote an encyclopaedia of alchemy around 300 AD.

After three centuries of activity alchemy ceased in Alexandria by the order of the Roman emperor Diocletian, who ordered that all texts on the subject were to be destroyed. But like many other forbidden practices it survived the attack. When, in the fifth century, the Nestorian Christians were expelled from Constantinople, they created new centres of learning in Syria, Mesopotamia and Persia, translating many Greek texts into Syriac.

United under Islam, the Arabs, between 622 and 750 AD, conquered Asia Minor, Persia, Egypt, Africa and Spain. Then, influenced by the Abbasid Caliphs of Baghdad, they settled down to acquiring as much learning as possible. Many Greek works were now translated into Arabic and somewhere between the eighth and ninth centuries the famous Jabir lived. His output was prolific but some of the works supposedly by him were obviously written in the tenth century, probably by his followers. During this period two other notable scholars, Rhases and Avicenna, contributed some original thoughts on the subject of alchemy. Both were doctors and Avicenna was the first to throw doubt on the possibility of transmutation of metals. Rhases carried out numerous experiments and broadened the classification of substances, which was a small step in the right direction. He divided them into animal, vegetable and mineral with a further subdivision of minerals into six classes, Bodies or Metals, Spirits, Stones, Vitriols, Boraces and Salts.

In the twelfth century alchemy filtered into Europe. Until that time contact with Islam had been limited to the Crusades but now Christian scholars turned to studying Arab teachings. The alchemical advancement in Europe was helped by translators like Robert of Chester who translated 'The Book of Composition of Alchemy' from Arabic to Latin in 1144. Another great translator was Gerard of Cremona.

During the thirteenth century Albertus Magnus, St Thomas Aquinas and Roger BACON all discussed the aspects of alchemy which could be classified as true science as opposed to those which were fraudulent.

Arnold de Villanova and Ramon Lull of Majorca were the reputed main contributors to fourteenth century writings. Whoever actually wrote the works attributed to Lull had a brilliantly logical mind and set down the various alchemical experiments in tables in which materials and methods were symbolized by letters of the alphabet. He placed great importance on distillation as a means of discovering the 'quintessence'. Distillation of wine was already known and the ALCOHOL produced was called *aqua ardens* or water that could burn,

Above: although by the 18th century alchemy had already fallen into disrepute, the idea of an elixir of life still held obvious fascination for some. It inspired J Wright's painting of an alchemist watching the sought after 'quintessence' distil into a receiving flask.
Below: an assay laboratory of the 16th century where gold and silver are being separated. In the foreground are stills known as pelicans being used on water baths, while an alchemist uses a set of standard weights on a balance for weighing out samples.

(also known as *aqua vitae* or water of life for its invigorating effects). Lull believed it to be an impure form of quintessence. Hence the first use of alcohol was medicinal. Alcohol was the first known liquid that would dissolve organic compounds such as fats and oils, which are insoluble in water. Experiments on alcohol such as this led to the discovery of the liqueurs, for example, Benedictine in 1510 by Dom Bernardo Vincelli,

Towards the end of the study of alchemy there was an interesting shift away from the philosopher's stone idea towards the medicinal qualities of substances. A Zurich physician, Paracelsus (1493-1534), campaigned for the use of mineral rather than herbal medicines. Glauber (1604-1668), a metallurgist and assayer, was not in hot pursuit of the legendary stone either but concentrated on the medicinal value of substances. He is still remembered for his discovery of what he called *sal mirabile* — sodium sulphate or Glauber's salt. These men are better described as iatrochemists (medical chemists) than alchemists.

Try as they might after 1500 years the alchemists had succeeded with neither transmutation nor the 'elixir'. It was time to look in other directions and after the publication of Robert BOYLE's 'Skeptical Chymist', 1661, alchemy went into a rapid decline.

Symbolism in alchemy

Symbolism in alchemy is not to be confused with the symbols of modern chemistry. The system of notation used by the alchemists was mainly a type of shorthand and varied with the alchemist, apart from certain popular signs such as those of the planets for their respective metal. Gold, the noblest metal, belonged to the Sun, silver to the Moon, copper to Venus, iron to Mars, lead to Saturn, tin to Jupiter and mercury to Mercury. This use of secret names and symbols for reagents and even apparatus may have arisen from a desire to keep their discoveries secret. Both literary and graphic symbolism existed with literally thousands of 'cover names'. ACID for example was sometimes depicted as a dragon.

Contribution of alchemy to modern science

Although alchemy contributed very little to the theory of modern chemistry, it has offered more to laboratory practice and method. Much of the equipment used by the metallurgical and medical chemists was developed and modified for alchemical practices, so that when scientific chemistry did emerge, there was a very wide range of methods available, the versatility of which owed much to the enquiring attitude of the best alchemists. Apparatus such as stills, flasks, beakers, condensers, receivers, water baths, tripods, the pestle and mortar, and stirring rods were common tools of trade for the alchemist. Methods of preparing chemical compounds such as distillation, sublimation, calcination, reduction, solution and crystallization were part of alchemical practice and are still used, in a refined form, in experimental analyses and industrial processes today.

Twentieth century atomic theory has, in a highly complex way, substantiated the vague alchemical idea of one ultimate matter, since the atoms of all substances are made out of the same kind of particles.

Part of the poetically inspired 'Ripley Scrolls' which are the work of the 15th century Augustinian Canon and alchemist, George Ripley. A still, above, full of alchemists busy preparing the elixir of life gives the 'spirit' which descends to inspire the sun and moon. Man and woman wade in the waters of life to find the fruitful vine and are surrounded by alchemists carrying flasks full of the water.

RONAN PICTURE LIBRARY

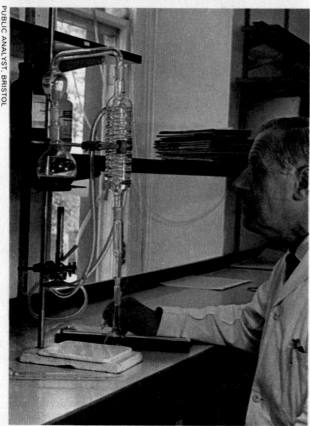

PUBLIC ANALYST, BRISTOL

ALCOHOL

Alcohol is most familiar as an ingredient of alcoholic drinks. But the alcohol found here is only one of many different kinds of alcohol. 'Drinking alcohol' is properly known as ethyl alcohol or ethanol. It is the only kind of alcohol that is drinkable in any quantity, though it can be fatal in large doses. But even small amounts of other alcohols cause brain damage and death.

Industrial uses for ethanol include its use as a solvent and in the manufacture of acetic ACID, PLASTICS such as polythene [polyethylene], ether, chloroform, and the tetraethyl lead added to petrol [gasoline] as an antiknock compound — though this additive has been or is being banned in many countries, since it is poisonous. Industrial applications account for approximately one third of total world production of alcohol with the remaining two thirds being used for drinking

Methyl alcohol or methanol (wood alcohol, so called because it was originally made from the destructive distillation of wood) is used as a solvent, in the manufacture of formaldehyde, and as an antifreeze. It is also used in *methylated spirit*, which is ethanol made undrinkable by adding about 9% methanol and very small amounts of benzene, pyridine and dye which by their taste, smell and colour reduce the danger of accidental poisoning.

Ethanediol or ethylene glycol (sometimes referred to simply as glycol) is also used as an antifreeze, to make various plastics and synthetic resins such as polyurethane, and many modern ADHESIVES. Glycerol (also known as glycerine) goes to make other plastics, EXPLOSIVES (nitroglycerine), cosmetics, inks and antifreeze. It is a by-product in SOAP making.

The combination of alcohols with other substances produces further wide ranges of useful products. For example, ethanol and chlorine combine to give chloral (sometimes used as a sleeping drug), which is combined with chlorobenzene to make the insecticide DDT (dichlorodiphenyltrichloroethane).

Many other types of alcohol are used throughout the chemical industry. Others occur naturally in plants and animals: cholesterol, a factor in heart disease, and vitamin A are both complex alcohols. Even the CARBOHYDRATES, such as sugar and starch, fall within the classification, though they are normally considered separately.

Structure of alcohols When one or more of the hydrogen atoms in a hydrocarbon is replaced by the hydroxyl group, -OH, the result is an alcohol. Ethane, C_2H_6, for example, becomes ethanol, C_2H_5OH. Hence the names for alcohols, methanol, ethanol, propanol, butanol and so on, corresponding to the related hydrocarbon gases, methane, ethane, propane, and butane. These alcohols, which contain a single hydroxyl group, range from volatile liquids to waxy solids.

Structurally, from propanol onwards the alcohols show isomerism — that is, there is more than one position where the

Top left: the distillation of wine was carried out as part of the alchemist's experiments. The alcohol produced was called 'aqua vitae' (water of life) for its invigorating effects. The long arm between the still and the receiving flask enabled the alcohol to condense.
Bottom left: a chemist determines the proof spirit content of an alcoholic drink. The beverage is distilled to free it from any sugar or colouring matter. The mixture of alcohol and water that boils off is collected and its specific gravity compared with that of known mixtures of ethyl alcohol and water. This enables the proportion of alcohol to be found.

-OH group can go, although the overall number of carbon, hydrogen and oxygen atoms remains the same. This structural difference can give molecules different characteristics, which means that they undergo different types of chemical reactions. For example, primary alcohols where the -OH group is attached to the end of a carbon chain can be oxidized to ALDEHYDES and to CARBOXYLIC ACIDS, while secondary alcohols are oxidized to KETONES. In secondary alcohols, such as iso-propyl alcohol or propan-2-ol, the hydroxyl group is attached to a carbon atom which is slightly more tucked away because it is in the middle of a chain and surrounded on either side by another carbon atom. There are also tertiary alcohols with a carbon linked to three other carbon atoms and a hydroxyl group.

Alcohols with more than one hydroxyl group are known as polyols. Both ethanediol and glycerol belong to this class. The molecular structure of some of these alcohols is shown.

Reactions of alcohols

Alcohols can be burned (for example methylated spirit) to give carbon dioxide and water vapour. They react with both inorganic and organic acids to give esters. This is the equivalent of an inorganic reaction between an acid and an alkali to give a chemical salt. For example, hydrochloric acid reacts with caustic soda to give sodium chloride. Similarly, methanol will react with salicylic acid to give methyl salicylate, or oil of wintergreen as it is commonly known. Alcohols can be dehydrated (water can be removed from them) to give ethers or olefins (alkenes) depending on the reaction conditions.

Production of alcohols

Most of the ethyl alcohol for industrial purposes is produced by the hydration of ethylene using high temperature and a suitable CATALYST.

$$C_2H_4 \quad + \quad H_2O \quad \rightarrow \quad CH_3CH_2OH$$
ethylene   water   ethanol

Methanol is made by the action of hydrogen on oxides of carbon using high pressure, moderately high temperature and a catalyst.

Ethanol for drinking purposes is made by the *fermentation* of sugars. Hexose sugars ($C_6H_{12}O_6$) are needed for the fermentation action in which yeast cells produce an enzyme (see below) which splits the sugar into alcohol and carbon dioxide gas. This gas causes the liquid to froth, which gives the process its name — fermentation from the Latin *fervere*, meaning to boil. The amount of alcohol produced will depend on the strain or type of yeast used and the temperature. Sometimes, in the fermentation of grapes in WINE-MAKING, the YEAST used is that present naturally as a 'bloom' on the skin of the grape. In most wine-making, however, and in the brewing of BEER, where barley is used as a source of starch and ultimately of sugar, the yeast is added.

Usually, starch in the form of barley, rice, potatoes or maize is hydrolyzed or broken down into a sugar, *maltose*, by the action of an organic catalyst which occurs naturally and is known as an enzyme. In brewing, the germination of the grain produces the enzyme. A sweet liquid or *wort* results and this is turned into glucose by another enzyme, maltase, which is found in yeast. The glucose is turned into alcohol by a third enzyme, zymase, also found in yeast. Dilute acid or alkali may be used instead of enzymes to convert starch to sugars.

Right: Distillation columns at a large petrochemical plant producing mixtures of the higher alcohols, so called because they have from 7 to 12 carbon atoms and hence a greater molecular weight than ethanol. Known as the 'oxo' process, it uses propylene as the raw material.

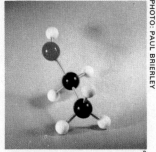

PHOTO: PAUL BRIERLEY

Above: Molecular models showing some simple examples of the alcohol family and the hydrocarbon gas ethane which is related to the alcohol ethanol. The black spheres represent the carbon atoms, the red ones oxygen and the small white ones hydrogen. A is the ethane molecule, B ethanol — a very important member of the alcohol group. The hydroxyl group is represented by the red oxygen atom bonded to a hydrogen atom. D is n-propanol, with a three carbon chain and the hydroxyl group attached to an end carbon atom. It could, however, be positioned on an inside carbon atom in the chain, in this case the centre one. This is known as isomerism; see model C, iso-propanol. E is glycerol, with three hydroxyl groups, and F ethylene glycol.

BASF.

ALDEHYDE

Aldehydes are organic compounds closely related to ALCOHOLS and CARBOXYLIC ACIDS. They are represented by the general formula R.CHO where R stands for an organic radical — a group of atoms in a molecule such as CH_3^-, the methyl group. The exception is formaldehyde, where R is simply a hydrogen atom. Formaldehyde is a valuable raw material for making plastics.

The word aldehyde is derived from the mediaeval Latin *alcohol dehydrogenatus*, because by removing some of the hydrogen atoms from an alcohol an aldehyde is obtained. This can be done by heating, using a catalyst to speed up the reaction, or by the oxidation of a primary alcohol using oxygen from the air and a heated CATALYST such as silver, copper or platinum:

$$2R.CH_2OH + O_2 \rightarrow 2R.CHO + 4H_2O$$
Primary alcohol + oxygen → aldehyde + water

The oxidation must be carefully controlled, or the aldehyde will also be oxidized to a carboxylic acid:

$$2R.CHO + O_2 \rightarrow 2R.COOH$$
aldehyde + oxygen → carboxylic acid

Other ways of preparing aldehydes are oxidation of primary alcohols using oxidizing chemical agents such as chromic or dilute sulphuric acid, and by combining carbon monoxide gas with hydrogen gas using high temperature, high pressure and a suitable catalyst.

Aldehydes are generally named after their related acid, so formaldehyde takes its name from formic acid. An alternative system exists where they are named after their corresponding alcohol: hence methanal is named after its alcohol, methanol, and is another name for formaldehyde.

It is the carbonyl grouping -CO in an aldehyde that makes aldehydes very reactive and therefore useful building blocks when forming new organic compounds, both in the laboratory and in nature. But the larger the attached group, R, the slower their reactions are. The first and lightest member of the aldehyde family, formaldehyde, is a gas and the others progress through liquids to solids as the weight of their molecules increases.

Formaldehyde, H.CHO, the simplest aldehyde, is readily made by adding oxygen to methanol using a catalyst. It is a gas with a very pungent and penetrating odour. It is extremely soluble in water, a 35% to 40% solution being known as formalin. This is used to preserve anatomical specimens. A stronger solution of formaldehyde tends to deposit a white solid polymer, a combination of several molecules that link together in a 'chain' to form one large molecule of varied molecular weight. It is called paraformaldehyde, $(CH_2O)_n$, where n is the number of molecules that combine. On cooling, formaldehyde gas gives another polymer, metaformaldehyde, $(CH_3O)_3$. Both revert to formaldehyde on heating.

Formaldehyde is a powerful germicide and commercially is very important in plastics. Many of the well known PLASTICS are polymers formed by the condensation of formaldehyde with phenol (to make Bakelite), or urea or melamine.

Acetaldehyde, CH_3CHO, is a liquid which boils at 21 °C and mixes readily with water. It is made commercially from acetylene gas and water, using a catalyst, and is used for the production of acetic ACID.

$$C_2H_2 + H_2O \rightarrow CH_3CHO$$
acetylene + water → acetaldehyde

Acetaldehyde also polymerizes when treated with concentrated sulphuric acid. At room temperature paraldehyde, $(CH_3CHO)_3$, is formed; this is a liquid used as an anaesthetic and sedative. Metaldehyde, $(CH_3CHO)_4$, is formed at 0°C. It is a volatile solid which is sometimes used as a smokeless fuel by campers.

Chloral, CCl_3CHO, is a pungent smelling, oily liquid made by treating warm ethyl alcohol with chlorine gas. It is used in the manufacture of DDT.

Benzaldehyde, C_6H_5CHO, is a colourless liquid with a pleasant almond odour, which is the main constituent of oil of bitter almonds. When amygdalin, a complex sugar found in bitter almonds, is split into its chemical constituents, benzaldehyde is obtained. On a commercial scale it is made by the catalytic oxidation of hot toluene vapour, $C_6H_5CH_3$, using air as a source of oxygen.

Benzaldehyde is used as a solvent and in the manufacture of dyes and other organic compounds.

Below: a selection of zoological specimens preserved in formalin, which is a powerful germicide and prevents the growth of bacteria that cause decay. In the foreground is a Siamese crocodile.

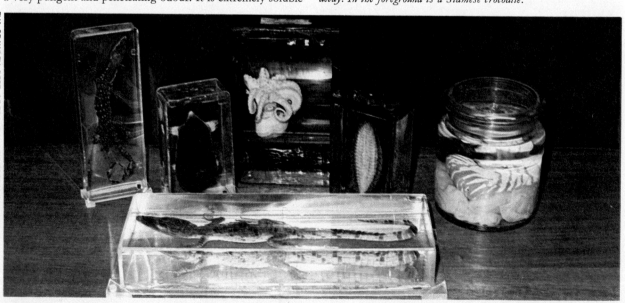

ALGAE, USES OF

The algae are a varied group of primitive plants ranging in size from microscopic single cells to giant kelp, a seaweed which may reach a length of 600 ft (180 m). In common with other plants, most algae contain the green pigment chlorophyll, but in addition to the green forms, algae may be coloured blue-green, red, or brown. They possess no true roots, stems, or leaves, and are characteristically soft and gelatinous. Some algae, however, such as diatoms, produce a hard skeleton containing silica, and others produce stony coral-like deposits.

In Japan, the delicate red seaweed *Porphyra* is commonly eaten, and is extensively cultivated. Another popular Japanese food is *kombu,* prepared from large brown seaweeds such as *Laminaria.*

A potentially valuable project is the cultivation of small aquatic algae, such as *Chlorella,* for large-scale production of food. After harvesting the algae, a flour-like substance is obtained which may contain 50% protein, or by varying the method of cultivation, may contain high levels of fat. *Chlorella* is only 4 thousandths of an inch (0.1 mm) in diameter and, under favourable conditions, there may be millions of cells in each millilitre of culture medium. Pilot plants have produced yields of 100 lb (45 kg) of dried *Chlorella* per acre each day, but so far, high production costs have rendered the process uneconomic.

Chlorella and other small algae are also used for SEWAGE purification. Sunlight causes algae to release oxygen, which is used by bacteria in the sewage to break down solid and liquid

KELCO COMPANY

Above: the seaweed harvester 'Kelsol' gathering giant kelp off the southern coast of California.
Below left: Euglena (×950 magnification), one of the types of algae used in the treatment of sewage. Using energy from sunlight, these algae turn water into hydrogen and oxygen, combining the hydrogen with carbon dioxide from the air to make carbohydrates, and releasing the oxygen, which is used by the bacteria in the sewage to decompose it. This is called photosynthesis. The red area at the end of the cell (the 'eye spot') helps it to detect the presence of light.
Below right: Macrocystis eisenia, one of the giant kelps from which alginates are extracted, grows in cool waters with strong ocean currents, which constantly renew the nutrients on which it feeds.

DR. CANTER LUND FRESHWATER BIOLOGICAL ASSOCIATION

KELCO COMPANY

wastes. This process is carried out in large, shallow lagoons, and needs a considerable amount of sunlight. Experiments have shown that the algae can be separated from the slurry, chemically treated, dried, and used as an animal-feed additive.

The US space agency NASA has experimented with waste-recycling and oxygen-producing systems based on *Chlorella*. Such systems would be most useful during interplanetary travel, and could reduce the amount of bulky gas cylinders and purifying equipment carried. The algae feed on carbon dioxide and excreted waste, and give off oxygen for use inside the spacecraft.

Agar-agar is a jelly-like material usually extracted from the red alga *Gelidium*. It is used as a thickening agent in food, and in the laboratory as a culture medium for bacteria and fungi.

Very wide use is made of the starch-like alginates which are extracted from kelp, usually *Macrocystis* or *Laminaria*. Their thickening, emulsifying and film forming properties make alginates important food additives. When added to salad dressing, alginates keep the oil and other liquids from separating. They thicken artificial cream, instant puddings and toothpaste. The inclusion of alginates in ice cream prevents the formation of ice crystals.

Artificial cherries can be manufactured by injecting a coloured and sweetened mixture of alginates into a solution of a calcium salt, where it solidifies into a 'cherry'. In medicine, alginates are used in surgical dressings, and as a binder in tablet manufacture.

Alginates are useful in many other areas. During DYEING, the addition of alginates improves the quality of carpets, furnishing and other fabrics.

A rather different algal derivative, diatomaceous earth, or kieselguhr, which consists of the skeletal remains of fossil diatoms, is used as a filter medium, a filler compound for paints, an abrasive in metal polishes and tooth-pastes, and as a heat resisting lining for furnaces. It was formerly much used for absorbing nitro-glycerine to make dynamite.

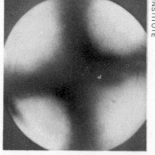

Above left: alginates are widely used in food processing. A research chemist is preparing desserts as part of a study of the requirements of the food industry for alginate products used as emulsifiers.

Above right: in the printing of fabrics, the use of an alginate emulsion thickener in the printing paste ensures sharp outlines in the pattern and rapid drying of the dye. A piece of printed cotton is shown at x6.5 magnification.

Left: these three pictures show the liquid thickening properties of alginates which make them useful as emulsifiers. They are taken under polarized light to reveal the structure. First picture: a drop of sodium alginate by itself — it is evenly dispersed. Second picture: the addition of a copper sulphate solution causes the molecules to align themselves (other solutions have the same effect). In this state the alginate can be extruded into a soluble yarn used for temporary stitching in clothing. Third picture: more copper sulphate makes the alginate solidify into an insoluble film.

ALIPHATIC COMPOUNDS

Aliphatic compounds are open-chain organic compounds which occur widely in products as diverse as petrol [gasoline], methane gas, butter, sugar and meat. These compounds contain carbon combined with hydrogen but often oxygen and nitrogen, and sometimes other elements, may be present. They range from simple gases such as methane (CH_4) to very large and complex compounds such as PROTEINS, which in addition to containing carbon, hydrogen, oxygen and nitrogen may also include sulphur and phosphorus.

Organic substances were originally divided into two main groups depending on whether they were related to the fats or to the AROMATIC oils (essential oils) and spices. The essential oils are found as the fragrances of plants and occur in flowers, fruit, leaves, stems and sometimes timber. The two main groups were known as fatty or aliphatic (from the Greek word for fat — *aleiphar*) and aromatic.

Later as the knowledge of organic compounds increased, a more exact system of classifying them into four main groups arose. These were aliphatic, alicyclic, aromatic (here, benzene derivatives) and heterocyclic compounds. Aliphatic compounds can be divided into various groups of compounds which have similar properties. The aliphatic compounds include HYDROCARBONS, ALCOHOLS, ALDEHYDES, ETHERS, KETONES, CARBOXYLIC ACIDS, AMINES, ESTERS, CARBOHYDRATES, AMINO ACIDS and PROTEINS.

This wide range of common household products is based on many aliphatic compounds: 1 wool — a type of protein known as keratin, 2 butterscotch essence, 3 linseed oil — a vegetable oil extracted from flax seeds, 4 red beans, which contain protein and carbohydrate, 5 methylated spirit, 6 olive oil, 7 carboxylic acid, acetic acid, found in vinegar, 8 the solvent acetone, a ketone, 9 the action of alkali on fatty acids is used in soap making, 10 skin perfume in alcohol, 11 cigarette lighter fuel, 12 a cylinder of camping fuel — the hydrocarbon gas butane, 13 cheese — over 50% protein and fat, 14 meat contains similar amounts, 15 melamine formaldehyde plastic, 16 starch and 17 sugar, both carbohydrates.

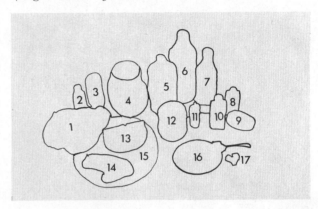

ALKALI METAL

The alkali metals are a group of ELEMENTS classified together in the PERIODIC TABLE, where they form group IA. In order of increasing weight of their atoms, they are lithium (Li), SODIUM (Na), potassium (K), rubidium (Rb), caesium (Cs) and francium (Fr). Sodium and potassium are the most important members of the group. All are extremely light, silver-white metals — lithium, with a density 0·534 that of water, is the lightest solid element. Caesium, the heaviest of the group, has a density of 1·87.

Alkali metals are all soft enough to be cut easily with a knife. They conduct heat and electricity well, and are easy to melt and vaporize at comparatively low temperatures, forming gases with molecules consisting of two atoms.

The metals are never found in a pure form in nature, since they are extremely reactive, and even react violently with water, forming hydroxides and releasing hydrogen. For this reason and because of their softness they are useless as structural metals, in spite of their lightness. Caesium bursts into flames even in moist air. Alkali metals therefore must be kept stored under paraffin [kerosene] or in sealed evacuated containers.

Their reactivity is due to the fact that one ELECTRON of each of their atoms is unusually easy to detach, transforming the atom into an ION with a single positive charge and thus giving it a strong tendency to combine with the negative ions of other elements. Although alkali metal salts dissolve easily in water, they are extremely hard to split into their individual pure elements. Alkali metals cannot be isolated by normal ELECTROLYSIS since this involves the use of water, with which the extracted pure metal would immediately react. Instead, it is done by the electrolysis of the compound after it has been melted to make it liquid. Mercury can also be used for electrolysis, though the metal then forms an AMALGAM, or solution in mercury.

The tendency of the metals to give off electrons makes them useful in PHOTOELECTRIC cells and TELEVISION CAMERA tubes, usually in the form of a thin film deposited on glass.

Lithium, Li, the lightest element of the group, is in some ways more like the elements of the next group in the periodic table, the ALKALINE EARTH METALS. In particular, its carbonate and phosphate are only sparingly soluble in water.

Lithium soaps, such as lithium stearate, are used as gelling agents to solidify greases. Lithium hydride is used as a source of hydrogen, such as for meteorological balloons:

$$LiH + H_2O \rightarrow LiOH + H_2$$
Lithium hydride + water → lithium hydroxide + hydrogen

Lithium salts are used in fireworks to give red colours. In medicine they have been used for the treatment of rheumatism.

Lithium is found in naturally occurring complex silicate clay and rocks such as spodumene, $Li_2O.Al_2O_3.4SiO_2$. From these, soluble lithium compounds can be obtained by washing the rocks with acids or alkalis. Then the sparingly soluble carbonate can be precipitated (solidified) and dissolved in acids to form other salts. Metallic lithium is obtained by electrolysis of the chloride, LiCl, fused with potassium chloride, KCl, to lower the melting point. The molten lithium rises to the surface and is collected under a bell to prevent it from coming into contact with the air.

Sodium, Na, is the subject of a separate article.

Potassium, K, is generally similar to sodium, though slightly more reactive. Like sodium, it reacts vigorously with water, releasing hydrogen, but in the case of potassium it sets

ZEFA

INSTITUTE OF GEOLOGICAL SCIENCES

Left: when lithium is heated it emits light of a characteristic wavelength and this effect is used in fireworks. A small amount of the salt lithium nitrate added to the mixture of chemicals gives a bright red coloration. Above: a polished crystal of the mineral spodumene which is a complex aluminium silicate containing lithium and is a useful source of lithium.
Right: a modern works for producing caustic potash, KOH, at Sedom, Israel. This process is based on the electrolysis of an aqueous solution of potassium chloride, which is found in deposits near the Dead Sea. Solid caustic potash is recovered by evaporation.

the hydrogen alight. Most potassium salts are less soluble in water than corresponding sodium salts.

Potassium sulphate, K_2SO_4, is used as a fertilizer, the carbonate, K_2CO_3, in glass manufacture, and potassium hydroxide or caustic potash, KOH, in the production of soft soap. Black gunpowder is a mixture of saltpetre, KNO_3, with charcoal and sulphur. Potassium bromide and potassium iodide are used in photography and medicine.

Potassium salts are essential for the cells of all plants and animals, and plants take them selectively from the soil. The carbonate, K_2CO_3, was first obtained by washing wood ash and evaporating the washings in pots, hence its name potash, and the 'dog-Latin' name potassium.

Potassium is found in many rocks and minerals, particularly in complex silicate clays, but can be extracted economically only from soluble minerals, such as sylvite, KCl, and carnallite, $KCl.MgCl_2.6H_2O$. Electrolysis of potassium chloride dissolved in water gives caustic potash, KOH, which can be neutralized with acids to give various potassium salts.

Metallic potassium can be made by electrolysis of molten salts, but there is a danger of its reacting with the carbon of the electrodes to form explosive carbonyl compounds, so the preferred method is the reduction by sodium:

$$KCl + Na \rightarrow NaCl + K$$
potassium chloride + sodium → sodium chloride + potassium

Rubidium and caesium, Rb and Cs, are found in the same minerals as lithium, and are by-products of lithium manufacture. Being heavy and easy to vaporize and ionize, they are useful for such schemes as IONIC PROPULSION in space, and MAGNETOHYDRODYNAMIC generation of electric power.

Francium, Fr, is highly radioactive: even its most stable ISOTOPE has a half-life of only 21 minutes.

ZEFA

ALKALINE EARTH METAL

The alkaline earth metals are elements that belong to group 2A of the PERIODIC TABLE. In order of increasing atomic weight, they are beryllium (Be), magnesium (Mg), calcium (Ca), strontium (Sr), barium (Ba), and radium (Ra). Calcium and magnesium are the most important metals in this group.

All the alkaline earth metals are silver-white and are good conductors of electricity and heat. They burn in air or oxygen giving a brilliant light.

The alkaline earth metals are almost as reactive as the ALKALI METALS. Their main differences are: they are harder than alkali metals; they are all heavier than water; some of their salts, such as carbonates and sulphates, are insoluble in water (except for those of magnesium). Alkaline earth metals readily lose two electrons to become IONS with two positive charges. These ions combine with negatively charged ions to form stable COMPOUNDS.

The pure metals may be obtained by refining their ores to a chloride, melting this and submitting it to ELECTROLYSIS, or by heating the metal oxide in a vacuum with a powerful reducing agent which strips off the oxygen.

Beryllium, Be, is the lightest element in the group and as often happens with the first member in any chemical group, shows some similarities to the elements of the next group in the periodic table. Here, it is aluminium, but it differs in that all beryllium compounds are highly poisonous. The metal has good mechanical properties and is used for the windows of X-ray tubes. Its transparency to X-rays is due to its very low atomic number, the number of electrons in its atom, which in this case is four. The atomic number for the light gas helium, for example, is 2. Beryllium is also used in alloys, and in particular with copper, which it hardens.

Beryllium is found in aluminosilicates (clay) such as beryl, $3BeO.Al_2O_3.6SiO_2$. Emerald is beryl with a trace of chromium which gives it a green colour.

Magnesium, Mg, is the lightest commercially available metal, with a density only 1·74 times that of water. In many ways it resembles zinc and cadmium more than the other alkaline earth metals. When burned, it gives a brilliant light.

Magnesium combines with nitrogen, as well as oxygen, and is used as a 'getter' (a substance to remove the last traces of gas in high vacuum devices).

Magnesium is used in lightweight alloys which usually contain aluminium. Well known magnesium compounds include 'Milk of Magnesia', which is a suspension of magnesium hydroxide, $Mg(OH)_2$, in water. It is used to neutralize stomach acids, and Epsom salts, $MgSO_4$, is used as a purgative. Chlorophyll, the green colouring matter in plants, is a complex organic compound which includes magnesium.

Magnesium is the eighth most abundant element in the earth's crust and occurs in many complex silicate clays. It is extracted from sea water and from the carbonate minerals magnesite, $MgCO_3$, and dolomite, $MgCO_3.CaCO_3$.

Calcium, Ca, is harder than lead but softer than aluminium and can be cast, machined and extruded. When exposed to air it tarnishes forming a layer of mixed oxide and nitride, which prevents the air from affecting the bulk of the metal. Like the alkali metals, it reacts with water to release hydrogen, but the action is much slower because of the limited solubility of the calcium hydroxide, better known as slaked lime, which is formed by the reaction:

$$Ca + 2H_2O \rightarrow Ca(OH)_2 + H_2$$
calcium + water → slaked lime + hydrogen

Calcium metal is used in aluminium and magnesium alloys, as a reducing agent in chemical reactions, as a getter, and for separating argon from the nitrogen in the air, since it combines with nitrogen. It is the third most common element in nature and occurs naturally as phosphate, sulphate, fluoride and carbonate, and in complex silicates and many other compounds. The most important mineral source is limestone, or calcium carbonate, $CaCO_3$. Other sources of calcium carbonate include marble, shells and chalk.

Calcium oxide, CaO, is also called lime or quicklime, and is made by burning limestone in kilns. It is one of the components of cement. When water is added to quicklime, this swells and changes to slaked lime:

$$CaO + H_2O \rightarrow Ca(OH)_2$$
calcium oxide + water → calcium hydroxide

Mortar is a mixture of sand, slaked lime and water. It dries and sets because the slaked lime reacts with carbon dioxide in the air to form insoluble calcium carbonate.

Slaked lime is mildly alkaline and is used in the manufacture of bleach, glass and paper. Calcium sulphate or gypsum, $CaSO_4.2H_2O$, is the important mineral source. It is used as a fertilizer and also in the manufacture of plaster of Paris, $(CaSO_4)_2.H_2O$. When gypsum is heated it loses some of its water molecules. The action is reversed by mixing the partially dehydrated sulphate with water and the plaster of Paris sets.

Hard water is water which has calcium and magnesium salts, such as calcium bicarbonate, $Ca(HCO_3)_2$, dissolved in it. These salts cause the scum and lack of any lather associated with hard water. The positive metal ions form insoluble salts with the fatty acid negative ions of the soap. The soluble calcium bicarbonate found in the water is formed by the action of water and carbon dioxide on limestone or chalk. The carbon dioxide in the air dissolves in rainwater, forming weak carbonic acid which washes over the limestone forming calcium bicarbonate.

Strontium, Sr, is fairly rare. There is a tendency for strontium to replace calcium in the bones of animals. This makes its radioactive isotope Sr-90 particularly dangerous, as bone marrow is very vulnerable to radiation. Sr-90 is produced in nuclear explosions.

Finely powered strontium ignites spontaneously in air. Strontium salts are used in fireworks to give a red colour. The minerals strontianite, $SrCO_3$, and celestite, $SrSO_4$ are sources of strontium.

Barium, Ba, is opaque to X-rays so a suspension of its sulphate, $BaSO_4$, in water is used for X-ray examination of the alimentary tract. All soluble barium salts are highly poisonous but because barium sulphate is insoluble it is safe to swallow. Barium sulphate, which occurs naturally as barite, is also used as a white pigment with high covering power. The more volatile nitrate and chloride salts, $Ba(NO_3)_2$ and $BaCl_2$, are used for green coloured fireworks. A film of metallic barium on the inside walls of vacuum devices is used as a long-term getter for the maintenance of a high vacuum.

Radium, Ra, is extremely rare and is found closely associated with uranium ores. It is radioactive, with a half life of about 1600 years. Its uses are dealt with under RADIOACTIVITY.

ALKANE, ALKENE AND ALKYNE (see hydrocarbon)

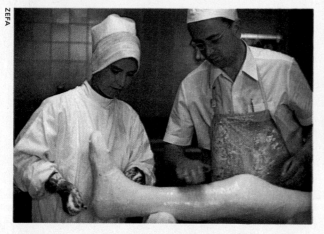

Left: barium sulphate is insoluble and opaque to X-rays. A patient is given a barium meal which follows the contours of the stomach. In this X-ray photograph a dark blockage is seen clearly in the centre of the bright white barium outline. Below: a fracture of the lower leg is set in plaster. Bandages impregnated with dry powdered plaster of Paris are soaked in water and then wound round the leg, setting to a smooth, hard casing round the broken leg.

Above: a lime kiln in Crete. Although fairly primitive it works well. The process is sometimes referred to as the burning of limestone. Crushed limestone is loaded into the kiln which is then fired. The heat decomposes the calcium carbonate into lime and carbon dioxide.

ALLOY

The first alloy, BRONZE (a mixture of COPPER and tin) was probably discovered by accident about 3000 BC. Today, metal components are invariably alloys, of which there are several thousand different compositions. An alloy is a substance composed of two or more ELEMENTS of which at least one must be a metal. Such a definition is, however, too general as no metal can be made 100% pure. Therefore, the term alloy is usually reserved for those metals where other elements are intentionally incorporated, and in a fixed percentage.

The value of alloys over 'pure' metals lies in the variety of blends possible and the consequent variations in strength, conductivity, temperature and corrosion resistance which can be chosen for a specific purpose. Certain pure metals may possess useful properties in their own right, but they seldom have the strength necessary for general industrial applications (for example, copper exhibits good electrical conductivity but is extremely soft). Small additions of other elements can greatly improve a metal's mechanical characteristics while maintaining its other desirable properties.

Making alloys Making alloys can be a complex process, depending on the number of different elements to be included and the precision of their required proportions. The simplest technique is to melt the ingredients together in the required proportions, but this is not always possible. When the melting points of the elements differ widely this can lead to extensive evaporation of the ingredient with the lower melting point. Copper, for example, melts at 1084°C (1982°F). Zinc melts at 419°C (787°F) and begins to boil away at 907°C (1665°F). When making brass, if the copper and zinc are heated together to 1084°C, both melt but the liquid zinc has already boiled away and evaporated in the air long before the copper has become molten.

To make brass therefore, the copper is first heated until it is molten and then the solid zinc is added. The zinc dissolves quickly in the liquid copper before extensive evaporation has occurred. There will be some loss because of the very high temperature so extra zinc is added initially.

Another technique for the blending of elements with widely differing melting points is to first prepare a 'master alloy' using part of the metal base. If, for example, an alloy contained 5% metal A which melts at 1000°C, and 95% metal B which melts at 450°C, it would be difficult to melt 5 lb of A and then try to add 95 lb of solid metal B. Instead a 'master alloy' of perhaps 50% each of A and B is made. Portions of this are then melted with the remaining base.

UNION CARBIDE CORP G.B.

Iron being poured from a furnace into a ladle containing nickel and magnesium. The magnesium boils and ignites in a 'magnesium flare'. The reaction causes the carbon in the iron to form nodules of graphite rather than the usual flakes, giving a very strong alloy called SG (spheroidal graphite) iron.

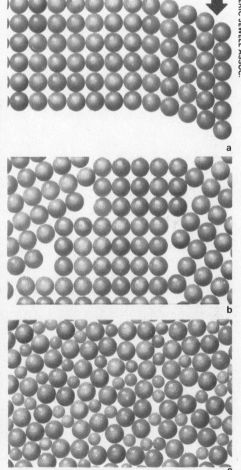

ERIC JEWELL ASSOC.

A: a pure metal bends easily because its atoms lie in straight rows. B: dislocations between rows allow splits to form. C: in a solid solution alloy odd-sized atoms distort the rows and toughen the metal.

Structure of alloys

The properties of alloys can only be explained by understanding initially the atomic structure of pure metals.

Although not obvious from their surface appearance, metals are *crystalline* in structure, that is, their ATOMS are arranged in regular patterns, a *lattice*. This means they form a regular network at fixed points arranged in a definite geometrical pattern. Such structures are mechanically soft because their atoms are arranged as if in flat planes or sheets which can slip over each other when an external stress is applied. If the stress is removed the planes do not slip back to their original place and pure metals thus have a plastic or putty-like nature.

In reality, the ease with which atomic planes slide over each other is the direct result of the existence of defects called *dislocations* in the otherwise perfect crystal structure. The role of dislocations in the deformation of metal crystals can be best understood by looking at the problem of moving a large carpet a few feet along a room. Simply to lift one end and pull could demand considerable effort and many hands. However, if a ruck is introduced at one end (the dislocation in this case), it can be easily pushed to the other end with the result that the carpet will have been moved by a few inches.

The presence of different types of atom in a metal CRYSTAL, whether introduced intentionally to make an alloy, or present as impurities, blocks the easy movement of dislocation and hence makes it much more difficult permanently to deform the metal. The amount and type of the added alloying metal and also the form in which it is present in the crystal structure control to a large degree the final properties.

Alloys are prepared in their molten state, then cooled.

Most metals are completely *miscible* — they will mix — in their molten states, and an intimate blend of such metals can be regarded as a solution of the constituent metals in each other. Metals *immiscible* in their molten states rarely make useful alloys, since they tend to separate like oil and water.

The behaviour of the mutual solution during solidification largely influences the properties of the resulting alloy. At one extreme, the mutual solution is undisturbed during solidification, producing what is known as a *solid solution*. Here, the alloy structure has a granular crystalline composition where each grain has the same composition as the molten mixture. Only a few pairs of metals, such as copper and nickel, can form solid solutions through the complete range of possible relative proportions.

At the other extreme, the two components can completely separate out during solidification, and in this instance the solid alloy will be a mixture of pure metal crystals.

More usually, there is limited solubility of each metal in the other so that the alloy consists of a mixture of two solid solutions or, as they are often called, *phases*. If as an example alloys of lead and tin are taken, one phase, usually called alpha, would be mainly lead with about 5% tin dissolved in it, while phase beta would be mainly tin but containing 1% lead. In this system the composition 62% tin and 38% lead is significant because the alloy completely melts at a sharply defined temperature like a pure metal. If an alloy of this composition, known as the *eutectic composition,* is polished and viewed under a reflecting microscope the tin-rich beta phase appears as very finely divided particles surrounded by lead. This alloy with its sharp melting point is widely used as 'tinman's SOLDER'. Another alloy containing 65% lead has a

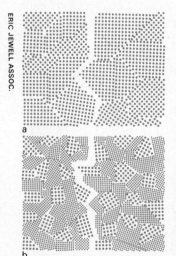
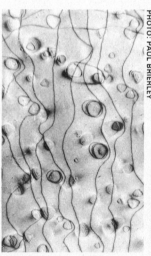

Above left: pure metals generally have large 'grains' and break easily along the comparatively straight boundaries between them (A). Many alloys consist of tiny 'grains' of their component metals (B). The boundaries have a more intricate shape, making them harder to break. Above centre: nickel-silicon alloy seen under an electron microscope (magnification x40,000). The dislocations (black lines) are prevented from moving by the small particles of the compound Ni₃Si.

Right: a high-speed steel cutting tool machining a metal surface. These hard steels may include up to 22% tungsten, about 4% chromium and small amounts of carbon, molybdenum and vanadium. For sustained hardness at red heat, cobalt is sometimes added.

microstructure consisting of comparatively large grains of the lead-rich alpha phase set in more of the finely divided eutectic phase. The melting range of this alloy extends over some 70°C (125°F) enabling it to be easily moulded during solidification. For this reason it is useful in such jobs as pipe joining and is often known as 'plumber's solder'.

Solid solutions have two different structures, *substitutional* and *interstitial*. In substitutional solid solutions, atoms of the additive metal replace atoms in the base metal lattices usually in a random fashion. A crystal lattice built up of cubes, for example, with base metal atoms located at each corner would have the additive metal atoms introduced haphazardly in a few of the corners. This is generally only possible where the materials have atoms of roughly the same size. But it is precisely the slight difference in atom sizes which hinders lattice movement and produces a hardening of the material, although the effect is not often very marked. Copper and NICKEL, for example, produce substitutional solid solutions.

In interstitial solid solutions, atoms of the additive element are lodged within the base metal lattice rather like small balls placed inside cubes where the main metal atoms are located at each corner. Often the additive element is a non-metal, such as CARBON or NITROGEN, the atoms of which are small enough to fit in the spaces of the lattice.

In some crystal structures the interstitial atoms form especially effective barriers to dislocations, and therefore need to be added only in small quantities. For example, the interstitial dissolution of merely 0.1% carbon in pure iron increases the strength of the metal more than ten-fold, turning the soft iron into hard steel.

There is one other type of alloy structure commonly found where two different metallic atoms form a chemical bond in some definite proportion (1:1, 2:2, 2:3, etc.). Such alloys are known as *intermetallic* compounds and possess a regular lattice structure. Intermetallic compounds are extremely hard and brittle, but when such grains are dispersed in an otherwise normal alloy solid solution, they contribute hardness to the toughness of the solid solution. Lead-tin-antimony alloys have a microstructure of comparatively large crystals of tin-antimony intermetallic compound set in a softer matrix (the crystalline phase in an alloy which holds the other phase) which is essentially a fine mixture of lead, tin and antimony. They are well suited for use in bearings where the hard intermetallic compound provides the wear resistance and the softer matrix enables the bearing to 'mould' to the exact profile of the rotating shaft.

Precipitation hardening Intermetallic compounds can also play a more subtle part in hardening alloys. One drawback of solid solution hardening is that at high temperatures the crystal lattice tends to be violently disturbed and this helps dislocations past the barriers of alloy atoms, so that the metal becomes soft. If an alloy which under normal conditions contains a small amount of intermetallic compound is rapidly cooled, the compound will be held in a *supersaturated solid solution*. Subsequent reheating to carefully controlled temperatures leads to the *precipitation* or depositing of the intermetallic compound in a very finely divided form throughout the solid solution. The small hard precipitate particles are themselves effective barriers to dislocations and what is more, they maintain their efficiency in this role right up to the temperature at which they begin to grow or redissolve. Another important advantage of precipitation hardened

Left and above: diecasting is a technique used for making large numbers of intricately shaped metal parts. It requires an alloy that will flow well into a mould to give maximum accuracy; here a zinc alloy called Mazak 3 is being used. The molten alloy is fed into a holding furnace (left) before being forced under high pressure into the moulding chamber where it solidifies. The mould is then opened and the casting forced out by ejector pins. Finally, it is cooled in a water bath.

alloys is that the supersaturated solid solution is often comparatively soft so that the alloy can be easily shaped before the final hardening treatment.

Heat treatment of steel There is one particular type of supersaturated solid solution which plays an important part in the HEAT TREATMENT of steels. When a steel is rapidly cooled from above 800°C by *quenching* in cold oil, a characteristic structure change, which normally occurs around 700°C, is not given time to take place. (It involves the movement of carbon atoms through the iron to create regions of iron carbide and therefore requires time at an elevated temperature). Under these conditions of quenching the structure change finally occurs just above room temperature in a haphazard manner, so that the carbon atoms distort the lattice to such an extent that the movement of dislocations become exceedingly difficult.

Steel treated in this way is known as *martensite* and is very hard indeed, but it is not particularly useful in this condition because associated with the extreme hardness is brittleness. This behaviour illustrates the compromise involved in alloy design: strength can be increased by alloy additions but if it is increased beyond a certain level the metallurgist pays the price in loss of toughness. The brittleness of martensitic steel can be overcome by *tempering* (reheating to a high temperature between 500°C and 700°C), followed by slow cooling. This restores toughness without too marked a loss in strength as the precipitates contribute to the hardening.

Common alloys *Bronze* is the oldest alloy produced by man, and is a copper-tin blend roughly in the proportions ten to one by weight. Another copper alloy is *brass* containing between 10% and 45% zinc by weight. *Cast iron* (pig iron) is an impure form of iron containing between 2% and 4.5% carbon and traces of manganese, phosphorus, silicon and sulphur. *Cast iron alloys* contain alloying elements such as nickel, chromium and molybdenum, which have been added to modify the properties of basic cast iron. *Steel* is essentially an iron-carbon alloy containing less than 2% carbon, less than 1% manganese and even smaller amounts of silicon, phosphorus, sulphur and oxygen. *Alloy steels* typically contain the following elements, roughly in these proportions: chromium or nickel, 0.4% or more; molybdenum, tungsten or vanadium, 0.1% or more; manganese, 10% or more. 18-8 *Stainless steel* contains 18% chromium which forms a tough, thin, oxide film on the surface. This transparent film protects the iron from rusting. The inclusion of 8% nickel enables the alloy to be easily worked. It is used for making a variety of household products from kitchen sinks to cutlery. *Nimonic alloys* are based on nickel with additions of aluminium, titanium and molybdenum. They are particularly good at resisting deformation at high temperatures and find an important application in gas turbine blades. *Aluminium alloys* are designed for a variety of specialist tasks where a strong, low-weight material is essential. Silicon, copper and magnesium are used as alloying elements, usually with small amounts of other elements such as manganese, zinc, titanium and nickel. One of the first aluminium alloys to be manufactured was Duralumin, a tough, light and strong material used in the construction of the Zeppelin AIRSHIPS and (in modified form) in modern aircraft. Duralumin contains about 4% copper and small amounts of magnesium, manganese and silicon. Other applications of aluminium alloys include electrical apparatus and cooking utensils. *Amalgams* are mercury-based alloys used extensively in DENTISTRY.

The ESR (electro-slag refining) process for refining alloys produced by other processes. An ingot of the alloy (large silver cylinder) is slowly lowered into a bath of molten slag formulated to react with and purify it. An electric current is passed through the ingot, melting it and allowing purified alloy to collect at the bottom of the slag bath.

ALTERNATING CURRENT and voltage

Direct Current (DC) electricity, such as is supplied by a battery, always flows steadily in the same direction along a wire. Alternating current (AC) electricity, however, which is used for mains supplies in most countries, flows first in one direction then the other, reversing its flow at a certain frequency — usually 50 or 60 cycles a second (written 50 or 60 Hz).

For a 50 Hz frequency, the current builds up to a maximum in one direction and drops to zero in the first hundredth of a second. It builds up to a peak in the opposite direction and drops to zero again in the next hundredth of a second, making a fiftieth of a second for the entire cycle.

A light bulb or an electric heating element works equally well whichever way the current is flowing, and so do electric motors designed for AC operation. So the fact that the current oscillates is quite unimportant in practice.

The advantages of AC rather than DC power supply is that its voltage can be stepped up or down using TRANSFORMERS, which have no moving parts. AC motors and alternators (AC generators) have no commutators — divided metal slip-rings for picking up the current — and are thus more reliable than their DC counterparts, which do have commutators. The frequency is chosen as a compromise between the conflicting requirements of transformers, power lines, lighting, rotating

NIGEL OSBORNE/JAMES MARKS

machinery and so. In Britain, Australia, New Zealand and South Africa it is 50 Hz (cycles per second); in the US and Canada it is 60 Hz.

The voltage of AC Most countries, including Britain, have mains electricity supplied at about 240 volts (the US and Canada are exceptions, with 110 V). But this voltage cannot be measured as simply as a DC voltage.

In fact, a '240 V' AC supply rises to 339 V at the peak of its oscillation. Furthermore, since the voltage rises to a peak in opposite directions alternately (+339 V and –339 V) its average value is 0 V. This is shown in the purple line in the graph on this page, which plots the voltage of a 240 V AC supply against time — the shape of the wave is called a SINE WAVE.

The effective average voltage produced by an alternator is that which would be produced by applying the same driving power to a DC generator of the same size. It can be found by the simple mathematical procedure of squaring the peak value — since the square of a negative number is a positive number, this produces an all positive result (green line). The resulting value is then halved to give its mean (average) value (+0.5) and the square root of this is then taken (+0.707). 0.707 of 339 is 240. This value is known as the RMS (root mean square) voltage, and is the one that will be registered by an AC voltmeter connected to the mains supply.

Three phase supply The form of AC described above is called single phase, and is the type supplied by the ordinary domestic mains. But the alternators at a power station supply what is known as three phase electricity. This is a way of supplying three times as much electricity along three wires as can be supplied through two, without having to increase the thickness of the wires. Three phase electricity is used in industry to drive motors and other devices designed to use it. These show the same saving in wiring for a given load.

The power station alternators have three coils equally spaced around the machine, and each of these produces a 50 Hz AC supply which is supplied to a separate wire. The way these three supplies alternate together is shown by the red, blue and yellow lines in the diagram. As the voltage in one wire reaches its peak, it is halfway to peak in the other direction in the other two wires, so that in effect each 'burst' of electricity travels out along one wire and returns divided equally between the other two to complete the circuit.

The alternators are wound as shown in the diagram. If exactly the same amount of electricity were drawn from each phase wire, there would be no need for more than three electrical connections. But in practice, the three phase supply, its voltage suitably stepped down by transformers, is converted to single phase by connecting one of the phase wires to one third of the houses in a particular area.

Inevitably, the load is never quite equally balanced between the houses, which means that an imbalance of voltage builds up between the phase wires. This is overcome by earthing [grounding] the connection between the three phases at the alternator and all transformers along the line by means of a neutral wire. The surplus voltage balances itself by conduction through the ground.

Domestic single-phase AC is supplied through one phase wire and a neutral wire running back to the transformer at the local substation. This neutral connection is not the same as the separate earth [ground] used in electric power sockets in Britain and many other countries (though not in the US) — this is an additional safety device.

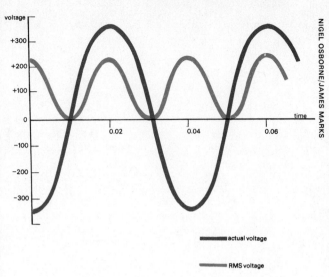

The RMS voltage of an alternating current is a theoretical value lower than the actual peak voltage; in the case of a 240 V RMS supply the peak value is 339 V.

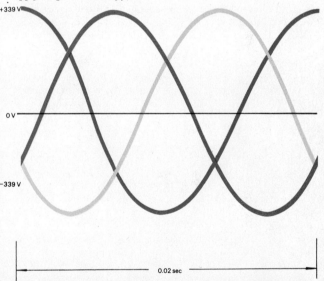

Three phase AC, as supplied by a power station alternator, consists of three supplies along separate wires and each reaching a peak in turn within one fiftieth of a second.

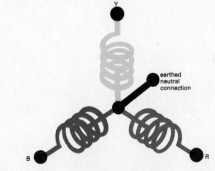

To produce three phase AC, the stator coils of an alternator are wound as shown. The neutral connection is to correct any temporary imbalance between the windings caused by unequal demand.

ALTERNATOR

The alternator, like the DYNAMO, changes mechanical energy into electrical energy. The form of output, however, differs for each.

Current from the dynamo flows in the same direction all the time, but from the alternator it changes direction at a constant rate in the form of a SINE WAVE. An ALTERNATING CURRENT like this rises to a peak value, falls to zero, rises to a peak in the opposite direction and then falls to zero again. This cycle is repeated 50 or 60 times per second in a typical power station alternator — that is, a frequency of 50 or 60 Hz.

The simplest alternator is much like a simple dynamo: a loop of wire rotates between the poles of a permanent magnet, the output current being removed from the wire loop through two *slip rings* which rotate against 'brushes' — spring loaded carbon blocks. The direction of current flow will depend on which way each half of the wire loop is cutting the magnetic lines of force. As one half descends across the face of the north pole of the magnet, the current will flow one way but will flow the opposite way when it moves upwards over the face of the magnet's south pole.

A complete cycle will be generated when the loop moves through a full 360° of rotation. Thus to generate alternating current at 50 Hz, the loop would have to turn at 50 revolutions per second or 3000 revs/minute.

Power station alternators In power stations—and even in the small alternators found in modern cars — the role

of the rotating loop — the *rotor* — and that of the permanent magnet — the *stator* — are reversed. Thus the alternator can be imagined essentially as a magnet — in practice an ELECTROMAGNET — rotating inside coils of wire.

There are two main reasons for arranging the machine like this. The first is that the heat generated in the rotor as a by-product of electrical power production would be difficult to remove, but the heat of a fixed stator can be removed relatively easily. The second reason is simply that the mechanical problems of conducting heavy electrical currents through slip rings and brushes are considerable.

In big machines, large amounts of heat are generated through both electrical and mechanical causes in both stator and rotor so that efficient means of cooling have to be incorporated. Typically nowadays, the fixed stator will be water cooled by pipes running parallel to the conductor wires, while the rotor will be cooled with hydrogen gas, an efficient medium which keeps unnecessary weight to a minimum.

Providing a rotor speed of 3000 revs/minute is no problem in a coal or oil fired power station, where steam turbines are used. The rotor is a two pole electromagnet turning at this speed. The simplicity of this arrangement keeps efficiency high and manufacturing costs low. The rotor itself will usually be made from solid steel with slots machined along its length to take the magnetizing coils and their hydrogen cooling ducts.

Where maintaining this speed does present a problem, as in

Right: the brushgear of an early Parsons turboalternator. Built in 1900, it ran until 1934 generating 150 kilowatts at 2520 rpm. This design had rotating armature coils so that all the output current had to be carried by the brushes. There are four of these, made of copper gauze, for each slip ring (two of them are behind the machine). Carbon brushes are now used almost exclusively, having been suggested as early as 1885.

Below: arrangement of a typical alternator. The central rotor is an electromagnet (green winding), powered through slip rings which collect current from brushes, also shown in green. It rotates inside the stationary red, blue and yellow windings, each of which extends two thirds of the way round the rotor. This produces one cycle of three phase electricity for each rotation.

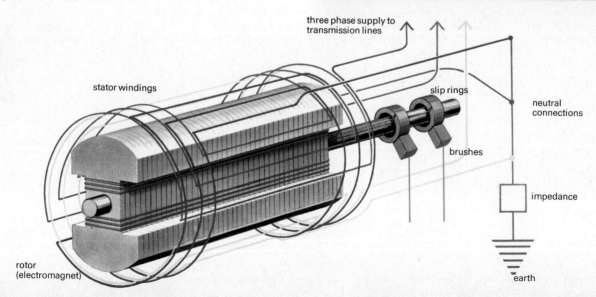

the slower turbines of hydroelectric power stations, the number of poles is increased accordingly. For the same output frequency, four poles would allow the speed to drop to 1500 revs/minute; eight poles would reduce it to 750 revs/minute, and so on. At such speeds the weight of the rotor becomes less critical, and the rotors of such multi-pole machines tend to be greater in diameter and shorter in length than their two-pole equivalent, thus making cooling easier. To produce the same voltage as before, the number of windings in each stator coil must be doubled or quadrupled.

Exciting For both types of rotor, power to magnetize them has to be generated externally by another machine. Usually, this external *exciter* is on the same shaft, rotating at the same speed as the alternator rotor. It either generates alternating current, which is then passed through a RECTIFIER to give the direct current required, or it generates direct current primarily.

In either case, this power will usually be fed into the alternator rotor through brushes sliding on slip rings.

This is not too much of a problem for small alternators because of the relatively low power requirement of the rotor — usually about 2% of the power generated in the stator. But for very large machines, with ratings up to 1000 megawatts even 2% (20 megawatts) would be a lot of power to feed in through slip rings.

For this reason, large machines use alternating current exciters operating with the rotor as generator and the stator as magnetic field source — the opposite way round to the main alternator — so that the power can be fed along the shaft straight into the main alternator rotor without the need for slip rings. A rectifier must also be built into the shaft.

For complete isolation from any external supply, the direct current needed for the field of the exciter is sometimes derived from a smaller permanent-magnet generator.

In power stations a typical alternator may produce electricity at several thousand volts, with a total power output of 500 to 1000 megawatts. The output is always in the form of three-phase ALTERNATING CURRENT, the stator windings being split around the machine so that there are effectively three outputs, each displaced from the next by one third of a revolution. Power in this form is cheaper to transmit than single-phase power and can be more easily utilized for driving industrial ac motors.

At the other end of the scale, alternators generating just a few hundred watts are now finding a place in cars and commercial vehicles. Because alternators use simple slip rings to feed their rotors, instead of the divided commutators used in dynamos, they can be run at a much higher speed relative to the engine, so they give high charging currents even at engine idling speeds. At the same time, because power is generated in the stator and not the rotor, they can be made smaller and lighter for the same power output.

ALTIMETER, ANEROID (see barometer, aneroid)

Top left: the turbine hall of a coal fired power station. In the smaller yellow casing is the exciter and in the larger one a 500 MW alternator. Behind that are three turbine casings: the farthest takes high pressure steam, the middle one intermediate pressure steam coming off the high pressure turbine, and the nearest the low pressure steam left over. This occupies the blue casing.

Above left: a cutaway view of a car alternator. The development of cheap electronics has made it possible to convert the output to DC quite simply. Here, a diode rectifier is incorporated in the unit.

Above right: lining up the segments of a generator armature. The ends of the current-producing windings are clearly visible.

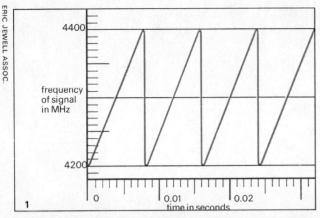

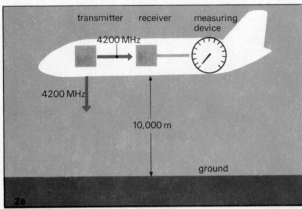

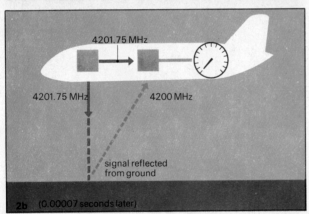

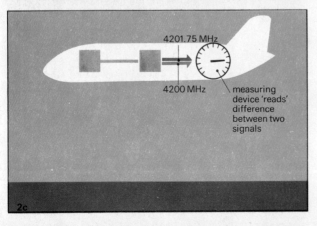

ALTIMETER, RADAR

An ordinary aircraft altimeter uses a type of ANEROID BARO-METER which measures the change of air pressure at different heights. Changes in pressure due to the weather can affect its readings. But because radio waves travel at a constant speed — about 186,000 mile/s (300,000 km/s) — radar altimeters can provide an absolute measurement of an aircraft's height above ground.

By pointing a radar aerial downwards, emitting a pulse of radio waves, and then seeing how long it takes for that pulse to be reflected by the earth and return to the radar's receiving aerial on the aircraft, a measure of the distance travelled by that pulse — and hence the aircraft's height — can be found.

The distance the pulse has travelled can be estimated from a display on a cathode ray tube or can be measured electronically. In either case it is only really accurate at high altitudes. As the aircraft descends nearer the earth, the time taken for the pulse to return to the aircraft becomes difficult to measure. At 1 mile (1.6 km) above the earth, for instance, the pulse would travel the return journey in about 10 millionths of a second. A pulse would thus have to be very short in duration to differentiate between the sent and received pulses. At an altitude of 100 feet, the time between sent and received pulses would be only about 0.2 millionths of a second so pulse durations would have to be unrealistically short.

Yet it is at such heights that altitude measurement becomes critical, and so a more complicated system known as an FM CW (frequency modulated, continuous wave) radar or radio altimeter has been developed. As in the simple pulse system, signals are emitted from a radar aerial, bounced off the ground and received back at the aircraft, but here the signal is continuous, centred around some high frequency such as 4200 MHz.

This signal is arranged to increase to another frequency 200 MHz higher at a steady rate before dropping back to the original frequency.

If a pulse is sent out at the beginning of this 'sweep', by the time it is returned the transmitter will be emitting a higher frequency. The difference depends on how long the pulse has taken to do the return journey. When these two frequencies are mixed electronically a new frequency — the difference between the two — emerges. The value of this new frequency is measured by electronic circuits. It is directly proportional to the distance travelled by the original pulse, so it can be used to give the actual height.

In practice a typical FM radar today would sweep 120 times a second. Its range would be up to 10,000 feet (3000 m) over land and up to 20,000 feet (6000 m) over water, since reflections from water are clearer. Accuracy would be within 5 feet (1.5 m) for the higher ranges but would be better close to the ground — within 2 feet (0.6 m).

The high cost of radar-type altimeters has prevented their use in many commercial aircraft, though the decreasing cost of electronics should make them competitive with barometric types before very long. Where low level accuracy is needed — as in blind landings — their use is virtually compulsory.

A modern radar altimeter works by sending out a radio signal of the shape shown in picture 1, with a constantly rising and falling frequency. A signal that has travelled to the ground and back will be at a different frequency from the signal that is going out when it returns. The difference depends on the distance to the ground, and can be 'read' by electronic means to give the height of the aircraft.

ALUMINIUM and its compounds

Aluminium, Al, is the most important element of group 3 of the PERIODIC TABLE. It is a light silver-white metal 2.7 times as heavy as water, soft but with good tensile strength, and is an excellent conductor of heat and electricity. Aluminium melts at 660°C (1220°F) and is easily cast, extruded and pressed. It is also *ductile* — suitable for drawing into wire, and *malleable* — easy to roll into sheets and foil. An aluminium structure weighs approximately half as much as a similar steel one of comparable strength.

Apart from its strength combined with light weight, aluminium has another useful property — resistance to corrosion. This is because of a thin hard oxide film which forms on its surface, protecting the metal from further oxidation. The oxide film can be thickened by *anodizing,* oxidation by an ELECTROLYSIS process. The anodized film can be dyed, which is useful for architectural panels and household utensils.

Powdered aluminium is used for aluminium paint. In the powdered form it is considerably more reactive than a solid block of metal, which makes it useful as a strong REDUCING AGENT to remove oxygen in chemical processes. When a mixture of aluminium powder and iron oxide is ignited, as in the thermite process, a large amount of heat is produced and the iron oxide is reduced to molten iron. This technique is used in welding steel and iron and in incendiary bombs.

Occurrence of aluminium

After oxygen and silicon, aluminium is the third most abundant element in the Earth's crust, making up about 8% of the total. Iron, the next most abundant element, is only 5% of the total. Like so many of the metals, aluminium is not found in its pure form but associated with other elements in rocks and minerals. An aluminosilicate such as felspar, $KAlSi_3O_8$, is the main constituent of many rocks such as granite, which is quartz and mica cemented together with felspar. These rocks are gradu-ally weathered and broken down by the action of carbon dioxide from the air dissolved in rainwater, resulting in the formation of kaolin, CHINA CLAY, $Al_2Si_2O_5(OH)_4$. Further weathering ultimately gives bauxite, $Al_2O_3.H_2O$ or Al_2O_3. $3H_2O$, which is a hydrated (water containing) form of aluminium oxide occurring widely and used for commercial ALUMINIUM EXTRACTION.

Pure aluminium oxide, also known as alumina, Al_2O_3, is found as corundum, a crystalline, extremely hard mineral. It also occurs combined with magnetite (iron oxide) a form known as emery. Both are used as ABRASIVES. Traces of other metal oxides present in aluminium oxide tint it to form precious stones. Chromium gives a red colouration to ruby, while cobalt accounts for the blue of sapphire. Aluminium also occurs as cryolite, Na_3AlF_6.

Uses of aluminium compounds

Crystalline alumina is used as an ABRASIVE, and in powdered form for column CHROMATOGRAPHY, an analysis technique in which a liquid mixture of compounds is allowed to trickle down through a glass column packed with powdered alumina, causing the various compounds to separate out at different levels. Aluminium hydroxide, $Al(OH)_3$, is precipitated as a white gelatinous solid when a caustic alkali such as caustic soda is added to a solution of an aluminium salt. Aluminium hydroxide is used as a mordant in DYEING. A fabric which will not accept a dye is impregnated with the mordant. The dye reacts chemically with this mordant, forming an insoluble *lake* and dyeing the fabric. Aluminium hydroxide dissolves in acids to form salts, and is therefore used in a powdered form as a stomach antacid. It dissolves in alkalis — few substances do both — to form aluminates. Sodium aluminate, $NaAlO_2$, is used as a *flocculating* agent to purify water and sewage by coagulating around impurities. It is also used in paper making.

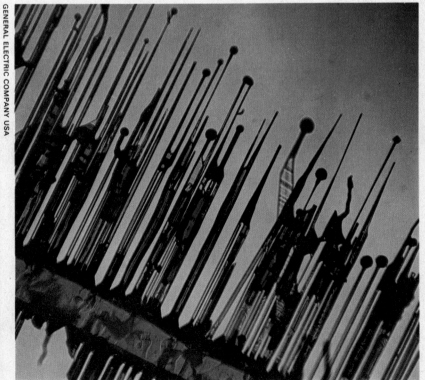

GENERAL ELECTRIC COMPANY USA

INSTITUTE OF GEOLOGICAL SCIENCES

Above: rubies (red aluminium oxide) before they are cut and polished by craftsmen.

Left: laboratory grown sapphire whiskers (blue aluminium oxide) are nearly perfect crystals that will take enormous stresses.

Aluminium sulphate, $Al_2(SO_4)_3.18H_2O$, is widely used as a source of aluminium hydroxide. It is also used together with sodium carbonate in foam type fire extinguishers. It forms double sulphates with other metals. They are known as alums, such as potassium alum, $K_2SO_4.Al_2(SO_4)_3.24H_2O$. Alums are used as mordants for dyeing and in paper making.

When chlorine gas is passed over aluminium foil a white solid, aluminium chloride, Al_2Cl_6, is formed. This is an important CATALYST in the synthesis of AROMATIC COMPOUNDS such as the process for making toluene, $C_6H_6.CH_3$, from benzene, C_6H_6.

Uses of aluminium
Aluminium is now the second most widely used metal, coming after iron. Aluminium and its ALLOYS, such as Duralumin, are used as structural metals for a wide variety of products from aircraft to cooking utensils. Aluminium foil is made by hot rolling followed by cold rolling, and is used in food packaging. Foil is also being used to replace copper wire in electrical windings. Other electrical applications for foil include use in CAPACITORS. Cross country electric CABLES consist of a steel core surrounded by pure aluminium. Pure polished aluminium is an excellent reflector, and does not tarnish. Aluminium mirror reflectors are used on large ASTRONOMICAL TELESCOPES.

Aluminium alloys have been used in buildings for cladding panels, door and window frames, roofs, and venetian blinds. Diecast aluminium cylinder blocks are used in a number of cars. Other forms of transportation where these alloys have been successfully incorporated are the superstructure of large ships such as the QE2, and on a much smaller scale, but where weight saving is equally important, in AIR CUSHION VEHICLES.

ALUMINIUM extraction
Pure metal aluminium is never found naturally. It is always tightly combined with other elements, and it has to be extracted from them. The only commercially significant way of carrying out this extraction is the reduction by ELECTROLYSIS of aluminium oxide, *alumina,* to aluminium metal. Alumina is obtained from the ore *bauxite*. Although bauxite is the only practical source of aluminium, the element is also found in other substances as diverse as pottery clay and emeralds.

Bauxite, called after Les Baux in France where it was first found, is widely distributed. There are significant deposits in Guinea, Jamaica, Surinam, Australia, the USSR and other countries. The amount of alumina in bauxite varies and only high grade ores with more than 45% alumina are worth mining.

History of extraction
Nearly 200 years ago Lavoisier speculated that metallic aluminium existed but neither he nor Sir Humphry DAVY some 20 years later were able to separate the pure metal. The first man to extract aluminium may have been Hans Christian OERSTED, who is thought to have produced a tiny amount in 1825. Aluminium was not made in appreciable amounts until 1852, when it passed from being a laboratory curiosity to being a usable but precious metal, costing more than gold. When the US Congress wanted to present General Grant with a unique medal they had it made of aluminium.

In 1886, Paul Héroult in France and Charles Martin Hall in the United States independently developed the electrolytic process for extracting aluminium from alumina. This process,

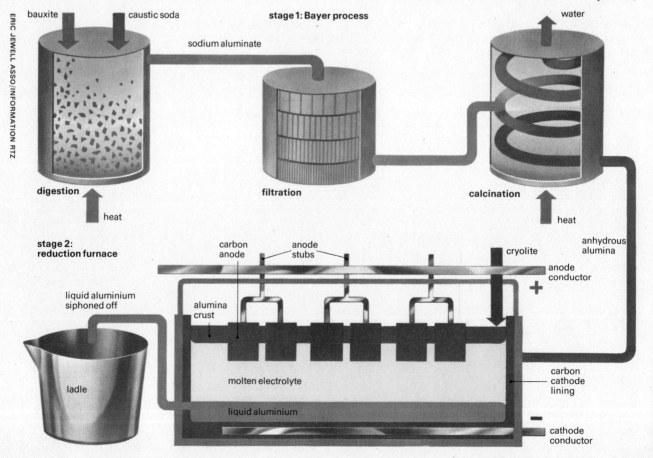

essentially the one that is used today, transformed aluminium from a precious metal for medals and similar uses into the common structural material it now is. A few years after the process was discovered world production was 2000 tons a year. In 1972, production was over 10 million tons.

Alumina from bauxite

Before alumina can be used in the electrolytic process it has to be produced from bauxite. This is done by 'digesting' crushed bauxite in strong caustic soda solution at high temperature. The alumina forms soluble sodium aluminate in the caustic soda but the impurities remain undissolved and can be filtered off. Alumina is recovered from the solution as a form of the oxide strongly combined with three molecules of water. The combination is so strong that it has to be heated to 1300°C (2370°F) to drive the combined water off, finally giving anhydrous alumina, Al_2O_3 in chemical terms.

Extraction by the electrolytic process

A low voltage, high amperage current of electricity is passed through a bath containing alumina in molten form. The alumina is broken down into aluminium metal which collects at the bottom of the bath at one electrical pole, the *cathode,* and the oxygen which reacts at the other pole, the *anode,* to give carbon dioxide and some carbon monoxide.

Because the alumina has to be molten and because it only melts at a temperature of over 2000°C (3630°F), the essence of the process was the discovery that alumina would dissolve in *cryolite,* a double salt of aluminium and sodium, and that in this solution, which melts at under 1000°C (1830°F), the alumina can be broken down. Even so, about two-thirds of the electricity used goes to keep the solution molten. Only about

Opposite page: the complete extraction process. First, bauxite ore is 'digested' in caustic soda solution, filtered to remove solid impurities and calcined (heated) to drive off the water. The resulting alumina is mixed with cryolite to lower the melting point and reduced to pure metal by passing a powerful electric current through it between carbon blocks and the carbon lining of the furnace.

Top right: mining bauxite by the opencast method.
Above left: a settling tank, where solid impurities are allowed to settle from the 'digested' bauxite solution before it is filtered.
Above right: a plant for making the carbon anode blocks of the furnace.

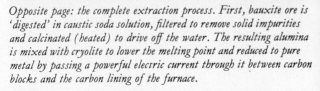

one-third is used in the actual conversion of the oxide to metal.

The alumina-cryolite solution is contained in a heavy metal cell or *pot* with massive carbon cathodes in the base. The carbon anodes, normally made in blocks about two feet (0.6 m) square by about four feet (1.2 m) long, are suspended above the pot and can be lowered into the electrolyte. Direct current electricity is used at only about five volts but the amperage is so high that specially heavy conducting leads have to be taken to each pot, and along the rows in which scores of pots are arranged. One modern aluminium smelter will have several hundred pots in total, each one holding perhaps 20 tons.

The overall chemical reaction can be represented by:

$$2Al_2O_3 + 3C \longrightarrow 4Al + 3CO_2$$

alumina + carbon → aluminium + carbon dioxide

The carbon comes from the anode, which is consumed and must be replaced when it is too short to reach the electrolyte.

The process uses large amounts of electricity. It takes about 8 kWh of electricity to produce one pound (454 g) of aluminium; the power used by one household in a year would not supply much more than a hundred pounds (45 kg) of the metal. Because of this, aluminium smelters are always near cheap sources of power. In the past, this has frequently been hydroelectric power but some smelters now draw heavily on nuclear as well as coal or oil generated electricity. On account of these heavy power requirements there has been recent interest in developing other methods of extraction to a commercial stage. In North America, a chloride method is now being used, and a process using lime is also being developed. These, and other new methods, only account for a minute fraction of total production at present.

The aluminium from the electrolytic process is 99.0% to 99.8% pure, the main impurities being traces of iron and silicon. Even purer aluminium, of 99.99% purity, can be obtained for special purposes by further refining.

The molten aluminium from the pots is tapped into insulated containers and taken to holding furnaces, where it may be alloyed to give it special properties. From there, it is normally cast into billets, slabs or ingots for further processing.

ALUMINIUM welding

Aluminium and its alloys can be joined by WELDING processes, in which the parts are pressed or melted together. In general, the techniques used are similar to the better known ones for welding steel, but there are differences resulting from particular properties of aluminium.

Welding difficulties The hard, persistent oxide film with a high melting point always present on the surface of aluminium is a great advantage in its use. It is an excellent protection against corrosion and other damage. The film would, however, prevent proper welding of aluminium if it were not removed, or well broken up, before starting.

The main difficulties in welding aluminium occur because of the properties of the oxide film. It has a melting point above 2000°C (3630°F); is insoluble in solid (metals form solid solutions, see ALLOY) or in molten aluminium; resists ordinary welding fluxes; and re-forms as soon as it is removed.

Less important difficulties arise because aluminium conducts heat about five times better than steel. It therefore needs more heat applied, since more is conducted away. In addition aluminium has a higher electrical conductivity than steel and therefore needs higher currents in arc welding.

Left: a line of 'pots' — the furnaces where the metal is purified. They run across the picture, taking up most of the width of the room. The curved strips carry current to the anode blocks; the large pipes carry off waste gases to be purified before being released to the outside air.

Above: the molten aluminium is tapped into cylindrical moulds. It is sufficiently pure for most industrial uses.

The basic methods of welding aluminium are gas, arc, resistance and to a limited extent, electron beam welding.

Gas welding

Gas welding involves heating the metal workpieces to be joined to melting point by a high temperature gas flame. Oxy-acetylene or oxy-hydrogen are the normal gas combinations. If more metal than that melted on the workpiece is needed for the weld it is supplied by a metal filler rod, also melted in the flame. The oxide film on the aluminium is removed by using powerful welding fluxes, which react chemically with the oxide at high temperatures.

Arc welding

Arc welding, the most widely used technique, depends on striking an electric arc between an electrode and the workpiece, using the workpiece as one part of the electric circuit. More rarely, two electrodes are used. Even when one electrode is used and the workpiece is part of the circuit, the voltages are too low to be dangerous: 20 to 100 volts maximum, depending on material and conditions.

Arc welding may be used with fluxes, in the same way as gas welding. But more commonly it is used with inert gas shielding of the arc, when no flux is needed because the inert gas, usually argon or helium or a mixture of the two, allows the arc to disperse the oxide film. The shielding gas prevents the oxide film from instantly re-forming at the weld by keeping out the oxygen needed for its formation.

Arc welding is faster than gas welding, is more versatile and is well suited to completely automatic operation.

Resistance welding

Resistance welding can be used for spot or seam welding. The general principle is the same as for arc welding. A current is passed through two copper electrodes pressed against the sheets of metal being joined. The softening of the metal and the pressure break up the oxide film and allow a firm weld. Special machines are needed for this method, which is used for thin sheets or small parts.

Electron beam welding

Electron beam welding is a more expensive method of welding but has the advantages of being rapid, and because the heated zones are narrow any disturbance to the metal structure is minimal. This is particularly important with alloys. A magnetically controlled beam of electrons is focused on the workpiece, the entire process being carried out in a vacuum.

Electron beam welding of aluminium is practical for both tiny INTEGRATED CIRCUITS and quite thick material, and has been widely used in the aerospace industry. Another technique, ULTRASONIC welding, is limited to very thin materials. Principally it is used for joining aluminium foil.

A small hand held apparatus for arc welding aluminium by the tungsten-inert gas process. The arc is struck between the tungsten and the workpiece while they are both shrouded with inert argon gas.

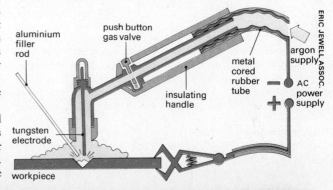

Above: arc welding aluminium milk containers by the metal-inert gas process. This uses an inert gas as in the diagram, but the arc is struck between the workpiece and an aluminium rod, which melts to fill the weld and has to be continuously replaced.

Right: electron beam welding in a vacuum chamber. This new technique is suitable for other metals too, but is still under development.

AMBULANCE DESIGN

Early ambulances were horse-drawn carriages built to carry stretchers. Around the turn of the century, motor ambulances began to replace the horse-drawn variety, but little attention was paid to the design of the vehicle other than as a means of transporting people on stretchers. Even today, most ambulances have serious disadvantages which are not immediately obvious.

With the recent discovery that up to 25% of all emergency fatalities die while on their way to hospital in the ambulance, it was realized that the standard of care, and consequently the design of the ambulances, would have to be improved.

Ambulances are rarely purpose built, but are converted from a standard design of truck or car. For example, in Britain many ambulances are based on the Bedford CF truck, while in America the Cadillac hearse chassis provides great comfort though with rather less space.

It is vital to have space and equipment in the ambulance to provide emergency 'first care' for patients, but it has been found in practice that emergency mobile operating theatres are inefficient. Performing a delicate operation at the scene of a road accident, with nearby heavy traffic and the lack of full hospital facilities, is too hazardous to be worthwhile. Consequently, ambulances are designed simply to transport their patients rapidly in the greatest possible comfort, while carrying enough equipment to deal with the most common causes of ambulance fatalities.

Ambulance layout Any ambulance needs plenty of interior space. It must carry bulky gear such as suction apparatus to clear blocked airways and oxygen equipment to aid respiration, and still have enough space to enable full first aid procedures to be carried out. For these reasons, large purpose designed vehicles are of more use than converted automobiles, though the latter may well give greater comfort.

Using a commercial vehicle as a basis usually results in a harsh ride. To improve this, a well-designed ambulance needs a long wheelbase, so that the patient does not have to lie over the rear axle; a low centre of gravity, to prevent the body of the vehicle from rolling when cornering at speed, and a low floor, to make loading of stretchers easier. These considerations mean that front wheel drive is necessary, since this does not require a bulky transmission shaft leading to the rear wheels. By using an automatic gearbox, jerky and awkward gear changes are avoided, making things easier for both patient and driver.

When adapting a chassis to an ambulance, an entire body is often fabricated from glass reinforced plastics or glassfibre, which is light, non-rusting and can be moulded to any desired shape. Storage cupboards and the bottle holders for saline or blood drips can also be made from this material.

One vehicle which has been designed to meet most of these specifications has been under test in service by the London Ambulance Service. It uses a French Sovam chassis intended for use in mobile shops. Instead of the usual folding steps at the rear there is an 8 inch (20 cm) step up to a gently sloping ramp. The side benches are well within the wheel arches, so that the patient's head is at the centre of inertia of the vehicle, where motion caused by the suspension is at a minimum.

Despite being adapted from commercial vehicles, ambulances are required to exhibit high performance and reliability. The wheels in particular take a great strain, and have to be inspected regularly for signs of cracking. The London Ambulance Service aims to replace its vehicles after 7 years

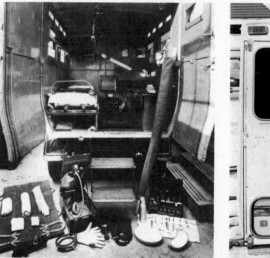

MARY EVANS PICTURE LIBRARY

GLC CROWN COPYRIGHT

HART ASSOC.

Left: the St John Ambulance Association, a voluntary service, used this hand vehicle for carrying a removable stretcher in 1882.

Centre left: by 1925, ambulances were comparatively well equipped, as this layout shows.

Centre right: the larger vehicle is the Reeve-Sovam prototype being tested on active duty by the London Ambulance Service, here compared with a conventional model which is in regular use. The new design has more headroom and easier access; the stretcher benches can be converted to 10 seats with arm rests if required. It has 40 cubic feet (1.13 m³) of storage space, occupied by the equipment shown below laid out at the side of the vehicle itself. This includes a stretcher for lowering patients from heights and rescue tools such as a hacksaw and wire cutters.

or 100,000 miles (160,000 km).

Electrical equipment Ambulances must have a comprehensive system for warning of their approach. A London ambulance, for example, has 13 lights to the front, 11 to the rear, and a two-tone air horn. To run these, and to provide power for the suction unit, premature baby unit and bright internal lighting, a heavy duty 60 amp alternator is needed.

One point which was overlooked in the past is that flashing lights are needed at the level of car rear windows, so that car drivers realize what sort of vehicle has suddenly appeared in their rear-view mirror.

In addition to the standard first care equipment, ambulances may be provided with electronic monitoring recorders so that on arrival at the hospital the doctors can discover quickly what treatment the patient will need. Many fleets are also equipped with two-way radios to enable them to be deployed more efficiently.

The last word Probably the world's most sophisticated ambulance is run by the International Grand Prix Medical Service, which attends motor races all over Europe. At these, hospital facilities may not be immediately available. Fifty feet (15 m) in length, the ambulance is virtually a miniature dust-free, air conditioned hospital. It has a battery powered X-ray machine, a hydraulic lift to bring stretcher patients into the unit without tilting them, a refrigerated blood bank and an operating theatre.

This massive device can be driven at up to 70 mile/h (113 km/h) although it weighs 24 tons. It has its own electrical generators and a self-contained hot and cold water supply.

Below: Australia's Royal Flying Doctor Service operates a number of ambulance aircraft to provide an emergency medical service over two thirds of Australia. It is claimed that a patient from the outback is frequently in hospital sooner than if he had been living in a town.

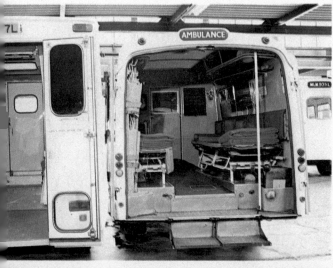

HART ASSOC.

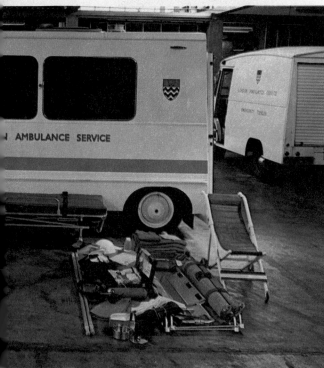

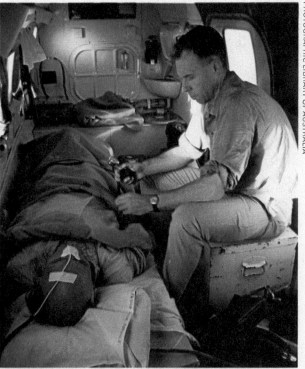

PHOTOGRAPHIC LIBRARY OF AUSTRALIA

BASF CHEMICALS

Above: reactors in a modern azo dye manufacturing plant. In the foreground are carts of prepared dyes before drying and grinding. Azo dyes are characterized by their brilliant colour, usually orange, yellow or red, and are used on plastics, leather and textiles.

SCIENCE MUSEUM: PHOTO MICHAEL HOLFORD

AMINE

The amines are an extremely versatile group of organic compounds, including substances that occur naturally in the human body, medicines, poisons and dyes. In chemical terms, amines can be thought of as substituted ammonias. When one, two, or three of the hydrogen atoms in ammonia, NH_3, are replaced by organic radicals (groups of atoms) such as the methyl group, CH_3, the resulting compound is called a primary, secondary or tertiary amine, depending on the number of atoms replaced. ALIPHATIC amines are slightly more alkaline than ammonia, their alkalinity increasing with the number of hydrogen atoms replaced. Like ammonia, they form salts with acids, and the action of caustic soda frees the amines from their salts. The lighter aliphatic amines are fishy smelling gases which, unlike ammonia, burn in air. The lighter AROMATIC amines are liquids and burn with a sooty flame. Aromatic amines are much less alkaline than ammonia.

Preparation of amines
A primary amine is formed when ammonia is alkylated, that is, made to react with an alkyl halide such as methyl chloride.

$$2NH_3 + CH_3Cl \rightarrow CH_3NH_2 + NH_4Cl$$

ammonia + methyl chloride → methylamine + ammonium chloride

When excess alkyl halide is added secondary and tertiary amines result. Alternatively, amines can be made by treating an *amide*, $R.CONH_2$, with bromine and caustic soda (R stands for an organic radical). A third method is to use a reducing agent on a *nitrile*, R.CN, or an amide, $R.CONH_2$ to give a primary amine, $R.CH_2NH_2$. Commercially, ethyl and methyl amines are made by heating their respective ALCOHOLS with ammonia in the presence of a CATALYST.

Aromatic primary amines are manufactured by the reduction of nitro compounds.

Uses of amines
Decomposition of fishy substances often gives rise to amines and all three methyl amines are found in herring brine. Ethyl amine is used in the rubber industry. There are complex amines such as the diacidic amines of which the *ptomaines*, formed when PROTEIN putrefies, are the best known. These are extremely poisonous and can be fatal to man, but what is popularly called 'ptomaine poisoning' is generally due to other causes such as bacteria.

Aniline and *adrenalin* are common examples of aromatic amines. The *alkaloids*, such as quinine and strychnine, are extremely complex cyclic amines (amines with ring shaped molecules). Aniline is used as a source of dyes and medicinal chemicals, the production of which depends on using aniline as a stepping stone by changing it into valuable intermediate products for the synthesis of a final product. Aniline reacts with nitrous acid to form *diazo* compounds. This diazo reaction is much used in the chemical industry. It is given by primary amines with the $-NH_2$ group directly attached to a benzene ring, the basis of all aromatic compounds. The diazo compounds are extremely reactive and therefore valuable for attaching other groups to a benzene ring by substitution to make various aromatic compounds.

Another important reaction occurs when solutions of diazo salts are added to phenols in dilute alkali, or are added to aromatic amines in dilute acid. A coupling reaction takes place and an *azo* compound is formed. Azo compounds are highly coloured, usually orange or red, and are used as dyes.

The first aniline dye, mauveine, was discovered accidentally by an 18 year old student, W H Perkin, in 1856, while trying to make quinine.

AMINO ACIDS

Amino acids are the building blocks of which PROTEIN molecules are made, and are thus the basic structural material of all living matter.

Although there are literally millions of different proteins, there are only twenty amino acids. Their molecules are linked together in a large number of different ways, and often in huge numbers, to form a protein molecule. Haemoglobin consists of the protein globin which is formed of 574 amino acid molecules, and a complex organic compound, haem, that gives blood its red colour.

The bodies of animals are constantly using up protein through excretion, the growth of hair and nails and so on. As a result, they need a constant supply of amino acids which the body can use where required for energy, and can build into protein. They do this by taking in protein, hydrolyzing it (breaking it down) into separate amino acids through the action of enzymes in their digestive tracts, and rebuilding them into the proteins that are needed. Enzymes are themselves proteins, and function like CATALYSTS in the body to speed chemical reactions.

The twenty amino acids are valine, leucine, isoleucine, threonine, methionine, phenylalanine, tryptophan, lysine, glycine, alanine, serine, cysteine, tyrosine, aspartic acid, asparagine, glutamic acid, glutamine, arginine, histidine and proline. Of these, the first eight are essential to man, since the body cannot synthesize them from other substances. A lack of any of them in the diet causes malnutrition. Vegetarian diets, unless very carefully planned, tend to lack some of the

essential substances. The list of essentials varies slightly for different animals.

The general amino acid formula is $R.CH.NH_2COOH$, with R standing for either a hydrogen atom (in the case of the simplest amino acid, glycine) or a more complex organic radical or group of atoms. This formula gives the amino acid an unusual property which makes it valuable in a living cell.

The formula contains both the acidic or carboxyl group, $-COOH$, and the alkaline or amino group, $-NH_2$. When an amino acid molecule dissolves in water it ionizes (becomes an ION) but because the carboxyl group has a negative charge and the amino group a positive charge, the resulting ion is electrically neutral. This unusual kind of ion is called a *zwitterion*.

If a positively charged ion, such as a hydrogen ion (H^+) from an acid, is introduced into an amino acid solution, it is attracted to the negatively charged portion of the amino acid zwitterion, neutralizing it and leaving it with only its positive charge. Similarly, a negative ion such as a hydroxyl ion (OH^-) from an alkali is attracted to the positively charged portion of the amino acid molecule.

This ability of amino acids to collect any stray positive and negative (and therefore acidic or alkaline) ions allows them to act as 'buffers' in living cells, maintaining the delicately balanced pH (a measure of acidity or alkalinity) which the cells must have in order to function.

AMMETER

The ammeter measures electric current. The unit in which this is measured is the *ampere,* with the *milliampere* and *microampere* used for very small currents. Current passing through the instrument moves a pointer over a scale by an amount dependent on the size of the current.

There are two basic types of ammeter. The *moving coil* type has a linear scale — that is, its divisions are equally spaced. *Moving iron* or *moving magnet* meters have a nonlinear scale.

The principle on which ammeters are based is that when a current is passed through a wire it sets up a magnetic field around the wire. Coiling the wire produces an ELECTROMAGNET whose strength is proportional to the current.

The moving coil ammeter has three basic parts: a permanent magnet, a flat coil pivoted at right angles to the magnet's field and carrying the instrument's pointer, and a coil spring. The moving coil and pointer assembly are pivoted, usually on jewelled bearings, and their rotation is held in check by the coil spring.

Passing the current to be measured through the coil sets up a magnetic field in opposition to that of the permanent magnet. This produces a force which makes the coil and pointer rotate.

Without the retaining coil spring, the result would be rotation of the coil until the two magnets no longer opposed each other. But the coil spring resists the rotation to a greater or lesser degree depending on the strength of the force twisting it. In this way, every position on the scale corresponds to a particular force and hence to a particular current.

In this form the ammeter measures direct current up to a fixed maximum known as full scale deflection — fsd. This can be as low as 25 microamperes in very sensitive instruments. Higher ranges can be added by *shunt resistors* connected across the coil. These then carry most of the current, allowing only a small proportion to flow through the coil.

The amino acids that make up proteins can be separated and identified by the process of electrophoresis. The protein molecules are split chemically into smaller parts, then dissolved in a weak acid that upsets the delicate acid-alkali balance and put on a filter paper. An electric current is passed through the wet paper, separating the individual amino acids, which are carried different distances across the paper. They are then stained and labelled down the side of the 'streaks' — Arg for arginine, Lys for lysine and so on.

Accuracy of such instruments is frequently within 1% or 2% of fsd, but much higher accuracies are available in laboratory instruments.

To measure alternating currents, RECTIFIERS which turn AC into DC have to be added to the shunt circuits.

A simpler and cheaper, though less sensitive and less accurate, method of measuring alternating currents is to use a moving iron ammeter.

In this instrument, the pointer is attached to a spring or counterbalance weight and to a piece of soft iron. There is another piece of iron fixed near the first. When the current to be measured passes through a coil surrounding the whole meter movement, magnetic fields are formed around the two pieces of iron, causing them to repel each other.

This causes the pointer to move against its retaining spring, but this time its movement is nonlinear because the repulsive force falls off as the distance between the two pieces of iron increases.

If an alternating current is passed through the coil, the direction of the magnetic field which it induces in the two iron pieces changes with the same frequency as the current. But as the force between them is always one of repulsion, alternating currents with frequencies up to 300 Hz can be measured as well as direct currents. The instrument's high resistance and other failings together with the low cost of semiconductor rectifiers for use in moving coil ammeters have caused the moving iron meter to fall largely into disuse.

Currents can also be measured on all-electronic instruments which have no mechanical moving parts. These generally function as VOLTMETERS, measuring the proportional voltage drop across a resistor to indicate current. They have the advantages of extremely high accuracy and a digital display, which is easier to read than the position of a pointer, but at the moment they are much more expensive than electro-mechanical types.

Below: a moving coil ammeter. The current to be measured goes through the coil via the terminals, establishing a magnetic field which opposes the field of the surrounding permanent magnet. The coil rotates against the force of the coil spring and so moves the pointer.

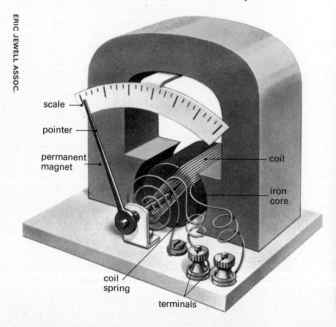

scale
pointer
permanent magnet
coil
iron core
coil spring
terminals

AMMONIA MANUFACTURE

One of the most important industrial processes is the manufacture of ammonia, which is needed for fertilizers, the manufacture of nitric acid, for use as a refrigerant, and as a cleaning agent.

Ammonia is manufactured from the gases nitrogen and hydrogen by the Haber-Bosch process. In most modern plants the nitrogen is obtained from the air, of which it makes up 78% by volume, and the hydrogen from natural gas.

$$N_2 \quad + 3H_2 \quad \rightarrow 2NH_3$$

nitrogen + hydrogen ammonia

Until the twentieth century it had been extremely difficult to bring this reaction about as nitrogen does not combine readily with hydrogen. The impetus to make ammonia came after Crookes' prediction in 1898 that the world's supplies of nitrogen compounds, which were in the form of Chile saltpetre, were being used up and unless an alternative source was found the world would starve for lack of fertilizer. A German chemist, Fritz Haber, managed successfully to synthesize ammonia under high pressure using a catalyst. A chemical engineer, Karl Bosch, later developed the laboratory technique into a full scale commercial process.

Theoretically, low temperature combined with high pressure are required to produce ammonia, but in practice temperatures of about 500°C (900°F) and pressures from 150 to 1000 times atmospheric pressure are used. This is because below 500°C (900°F) the rate at which equilibrium is reached is too slow. Unfortunately, at a higher temperature the amount of ammonia produced is low, around 20% at 250 atmospheres and around 50% at 800 atmospheres. By using a CATALYST the rate of reaction can be speeded up and more ammonia produced in a given time.

The catalyst is usually iron oxide which is often mixed with a small quantity of a 'promoter' such as aluminium sesquioxide to increase its effectiveness. The iron oxide is reduced

ERIC JEWELL ASSOC.

by the hydrogen to spongy pure iron when the process is started up. Over a period the catalyst gradually loses its effectiveness as it becomes 'poisoned' by traces of carbon dioxide, carbon monoxide and sulphur compounds. It is then replaced.

In the process itself the catalyst is packed into catalyst beds inside the steel reaction vessel which is designed to withstand very high pressure. The steel must also be resistant to attack from hydrogen especially under the high temperature and pressure conditions. The nitrogen and hydrogen gases are purified, compressed, and passed through a warm-up heater before entering the converter. Since the reaction is exothermic (heat-producing) once inside the converter the temperature maintains itself at the correct level.

The ammonia gas formed is liquefied by passing it through pipes cooled by cold water. Unconverted nitrogen and hydrogen present are not liquefied and are recycled.

Other methods of preparing ammonia commercially are from coal gas, and the cyanamide process where calcium cyanamide is sprayed with water to remove traces of calcium carbide, and is then treated with superheated steam which causes it to decompose into ammonia and calcium carbonate.

$$CaCN_2 \qquad + H_2O \rightarrow 2NH_3 \qquad + CaCO_3$$
calcium cyanamide + water   ammonia + calcium carbonate

Below: these three production plants have a total capacity of around 3000 tons of ammonia per day.

Right: the ICI quench convertor, a recent design. Gas is piped into the base and heated by passing it up and down the central heat exchanger. It then passes through a bed of catalyst, turning it to ammonia and creating intense heat, which it gives up to the incoming gas in the heat exchanger. Overheating is prevented by introducing quench, which is simply cold gas, through rings of perforated tubes buried in the catalyst. The pyrometer monitors the temperature.

ICI CHEMICALS DIVISION

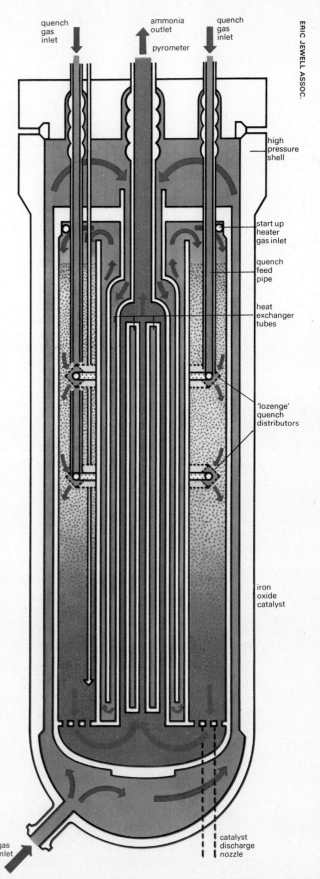

quench gas inlet

ammonia outlet

quench gas inlet

pyrometer

high pressure shell

start up heater gas inlet

quench feed pipe

heat exchanger tubes

'lozenge' quench distributors

iron oxide catalyst

gas inlet

catalyst discharge nozzle

MARY EVANS PICTURE LIBRARY

Above: this illustration shows workers finishing shells at the Royal Woolwich Arsenal, London, in 1862. The shells were of cast iron and filled with gunpowder. A slow burning fuse fitted through a hole in the case was ignited by the propelling charge in the cannon.

Below: checking shells in the shell filling factory at Chilwell, England, during World War 1. The shells had forged steel or cast iron bodies, and were filled with low explosive gunpowder (black powder) or with a high explosive such as TNT or amatol. Shrapnel shells contained steel balls which scattered when the shell exploded, and were very effective against infantry and cavalry.

AMMUNITION

Ammunition is basically any explosive device, from a tiny starter's pistol cartridge to a ten-ton bomb.

The word 'ammunition' is derived from the Latin *munire* meaning 'to fortify' and originally meant fortifications and the tools of war. From this stems a modern definition that ammunition is any military device which includes components filled with explosive, smoke, incendiary (fire producing) or pyrotechnic (illuminating) compositions. Such a definition, however, would exclude many other items, for example shot gun cartridges, distress and signalling rockets, engineering explosives, chemicals such as tear gas, aircraft ejection seat cartridges, and even fireworks, all of which can be considered as ammunition.

Explosives   All ammunition contains EXPLOSIVE materials in one form or another, and the way they function and release their energy can be carefully controlled.

Explosives are substances which can be converted into hot gases or volatile products, and in the process exert a sudden pressure on their surroundings. The speed with which this happens determines the precise application of the explosive substance. 'High' explosives react fast, usually within a few millionths of a second, and create a sudden and disruptive increase in pressure which causes a severe shock wave. The tremendous power released by this detonation can be used to burst a shell into small lethal fragments. 'Low' explosives are slower, taking a few thousandths of a second to react. The pressure produced can be used in a gun to propel a shell.

Typical high explosives as used in shells, bombs, land and sea mines, grenades and demolition work are TNT, gelignite, hexogen, tetryl and PETN. Cordite is a typical low explosive used in most modern guns as a propellant.

IMPERIAL WAR MUSEUM

Gun ammunition Ammunition for guns, whatever their size, comprises a propellent charge and a projectile. The two items may be secured permanently together (fixed), supplied as individual items and put together before loading (semi-fixed), or kept and loaded quite separately (separate-loading). The deciding factors are firstly the method of gas sealing or *obturation* adopted, and secondly the gun's barrel size or *calibre*. The charge is sealed off in the gun's chamber either by means of a pad fitted to the breech, or by enclosing the propellant in a cartridge case. Gas pressure from the burning propellant expands the pad or the case to completely seal off the rear of the charge. The projectile fits snugly in the barrel, thereby preventing a forward leak of gas. As the bore size of the gun gets larger so the charge and projectile become heavier and more cumbersome to handle, and it is necessary to load them separately.

A whole round of ammunition comprises the propellant or charge and the projectile or shell. For a typical fixed round the cartridge case is usually made of brass, 70 parts copper to 30 of zinc. The brass is moulded into shape in a series of stages, which toughen and harden the metal. By alternatively working and annealing (at about 600°C) the case can be made thick and hard at the base, to take the initiating cap and primer and to withstand the forces of loading and extraction; softer in the centre section, to expand and seal against the chamber wall; and harder at the nose so that the shell can be firmly crimped to it. Other materials, such as steel, aluminium and plastics, and cheaper methods of construction, are in use, but they have only limited application.

The propellant may be in the form of small grains, short or long cords, or a solid block perforated by slots or holes to control the speed of burning. It is ignited by the primer. This comprises a small quantity of a very sensitive explosive which is initiated, or detonated, when the striker pinches it between the cup and anvil. The flash is passed to a few grammes of gunpowder, which ignites to set off the propellant.

The shell or projectile has three main components: the high explosive filling, the driving band, and the fuze. Shells are normally forged from a good quality steel, the final shape being the result of three or more operations and some machining to required tolerances. The projectile's shape is determined by a number of factors. For a stable flight it should be no longer than five calibres, for low skin-friction it should be smooth, and the base should be streamlined to reduce aerodynamic drag. The driving band is a copper ring forced into a groove cut around the lower section of the body. Its tasks are to provide a good gas seal in front of the charge, to seat the projectile in the bore, and to engage the spiral rifling of the gun barrel to make the shell spin. The shell body is filled with high explosive, for example TNT. This is done by pouring molten explosive into the cavity, taking care to ensure no empty spaces are formed on cooling. A ratio of 15% explosive to total shell weight is normal.

The fuze is fitted to the shell last of all. It is potentially the most dangerous component in the round, and must be designed not to explode during firing, when it is subjected to typical gas pressures of 20 tons per square inch (about 3,000 bar) and accelerations of 20,000 'g'. Yet it must function reliably when the shell strikes the target. Like the cartridge it contains an explosive train: a striker sets off a detonator, the impulse is passed to a less sensitive but more forceful explosive contained in a pellet, and the detonation wave from this pellet sets off the main filling. Fuzes are extremely intricate and are designed to respond to the forces of firing and flight. Their

Above: 'Little David', a huge mortar of 914 mm (36 inch) calibre made in 1944 for the US army. It had a rifled barrel, and fired a projectile weighing 3700 lb (1680 kg) which was designed to penetrate underground fortifications. It was introduced too late in the war to be used with much effect, and its size made it a rather impractical weapon for most artillery purposes.

Left: part of a British army field ammunition store in Germany. The shells are used by the 155 mm (6 inch) self-propelled howitzers of the Royal Artillery and other NATO units, which have a firing range of over nine miles (14.5 km).

fuze

high
explosive
filling

steel
shell

driving
band

**fixed
round
with
explosive
shell**

gilding
metal
jacket

lead-
antimony
core

**small
arms
round
with
bullet**

propellant

cartridge
case

primer

propellant

cartridge
case

**primer
detail**

flash
holes

gunpowder

metal ball

anvil

sensitive
explosive

cup

**primer
detail**

propellant

flash holes

anvil

cup

cap
composition

lead
alloy
core

**tracer
bullet**

tracer
compositions

hole

cardboard
disc

shot

rolled paper
tube

**shotgun
cartridge**

propellant

brass
end

cap

Comparison of artillery and rifle ammunition, with details of the detonators, and, below, a tracer bullet and a shotgun cartridge.

mechanism can be likened to that of a combination lock: it is unlocked by the special signature of the forces imposed by the gun and to no other stimulation.

For separate-loading ammunition, where the gun's breech mechanism provides the rear seal, the charge is composed of sticks of cordite bound together inside a cloth bag. Sewn to one end is an igniter pad holding a few grammes of gunpowder. This is ignited by the flash from a small brass-cased cartridge fitted into a vent in the breech block.

Semi-fixed and separate rounds are necessary on guns where a variety of shell velocities are required, for example to produce a special trajectory to cross an obstacle (such as a hill or forest) behind which the target is hidden. For rounds of this kind, extra charges are packed in several small bags easily removed from the main charge.

Other types of ammunition
This basic design of an ammunition round is modified appropriately for other purposes. Small arms rounds do not need gunpowder in the primer, the small amount of cap composition being sufficient to ignite the propellant, and the bullet is made of a lead antimony alloy core coated with a gilding metal jacket. On firing, this jacket, which is slightly over calibre in size, performs the function of a driving band. ARMOUR PIERCING SHELLS have a core of steel or tungsten carbide instead of lead alloy. Tracer bullets contain compositions that burn in flight, making it possible to see the bullet's trajectory. They are used in machine gun ammunition belts interspersed among ordinary rounds to improve aiming.

For shotgun cartridges, the single projectile is replaced by a quantity of small lead balls (shot), their size and number depending on the range and spread required. As the gun works at low pressures the case need not be made entirely of brass, but only the rear portion holding the cap, which is bonded to a rolled paper tube containing the propellant and shot. The front end is closed by a cardboard disc, and the whole is lacquered to prevent moisture getting inside. Blank ammunition is normally loaded into brass cases and the propellant, often gunpowder, is merely closed off with a cardboard wad and secured by pinching the nose of the case.

The design of ammunition for guns is complicated by the number of components needed, and the aircraft or hand delivered types are simpler. The aircraft BOMB is usually thin-skinned, but contains a substantial quantity of high explosive, from 10 to 16,000 pounds (5 to 7250 kg), and the explosive to total weight ratio is often near 40%. Stability in flight is achieved by means of a tail and good aerodynamic shape. Fuzes can be fitted to either or both nose and tail, and can incorporate delayed action so that the bomb functions sometime after hitting the ground.

GRENADES may be hand thrown or rifle projected, and may be filled with high explosive, smoke mixtures, or tear gas. Fuzes are usually based on a delay train, rather than on impact principles, as space is limited. For rifle projection the grenade is placed in a cup attached to the muzzle, and gas pressure from a special cartridge propels it.

MINES may be mechanically laid or placed in position by hand, and may be designed to cause damage to the target by blast or fragments or both, or may include a shaped charge to penetrate armour plate. The fuze can be made sensitive to a variety of stimuli. Most types, both land and sea, work by simple contact. Non-metallic materials are often used in their construction to prevent them from being found by METAL DETECTORS.

AMPERE, André Marie (1775-1836)

André Marie Ampère was a French mathematician and physicist with wide-ranging interests and a phenomenal memory. He made contributions to mathematics, mechanics, physics (independently discovering AVOGADRO's law) and philosophy. But it is mostly for his work on electricity that he is remembered. The basic unit of electric current, the ampere, is named after him.

Born near Lyons, Ampère was the son of a rich silk merchant who tutored him privately. The young André showed a precocious ability in mathematics, and by his teens he had read the works of the greatest mathematicians. His father was executed in 1793 during the Reign of Terror, and André gave private instruction in science to support himself.

He married in 1799 and became professor of physics at Bourg from 1801 to 1803. There he published a small but impressive treatise on the statistics of games of chance. He returned to Lyons, where his wife died, and then moved on to a lectureship in mathematics at the Ecole Polytechnique in Paris. He taught there for the rest of his life, becoming a professor in 1809 and being elected to the French Academy of Sciences in 1814. Despite the loss of his father and his wife, which left him depressed for life, he had a warm and friendly personality.

In 1820 a meeting of the French Academy saw a demonstration of Hans Christian OERSTED's discovery that a compass needle is deflected by the passage of an electric current through a nearby wire. Inspired by this first basic step in electromagnetism, Ampère also began to experiment and in a few weeks was able to demonstrate further developments. Among these was the so-called 'Ampère's rule', that a current flowing in a horizontal conductor or wire pointing north deflects a compass needle to the east.

Ampère went on to show that when current flowed in the same direction along two parallel conductors, the wires were attracted, but that if the current in one conductor was reversed, the wires would be repelled. He showed that the magnetic force round a conductor is inversely proportional to the square of the distance. This analogy with gravitation led him to be termed the 'Newton of electromagnetism'. Ampère's laws were the foundations of James Clerk MAXWELL's 1865 electromagnetic theory.

In addition to the mathematical laws of electromagnetism, Ampère announced that a coil of wire with a current flowing through it acted in the same way as a magnet, and that a bar of iron placed inside such a coil became magnetized. He called such an arrangement a *solenoid*, a name that is still given to the ELECTROMAGNETS used in RELAYS and other devices.

Ampère deduced from his experiment that permanent magnets operate by the circulation of small electric currents inside iron bars, and that the Earth's magnetism reveals the existence of electric currents inside the Earth. These advanced ideas foreshadowed modern views of the nature of matter.

Right: A reproduction of apparatus which Ampère used in 1820 to show the effect of electrical currents passing through a pair of parallel conductors. The bar with the connectors at each end is fixed, and the other bar pivots in two recesses filled with mercury to give good electrical contact. The bars can be connected beneath the board so that the current can flow either in the same direction through them, or in opposite directions. When the currents flow the same way, the bars attract each other; when they flow in opposite directions, the bars repel. This principle is still used in defining the ampere.

Left: André Marie Ampère, as shown in a book by Figuier.

Below: an apparatus to show the motion of a conductor in a magnetic field. The frame, with arrows showing the flow of the current, is pivoted on A and B.

If the bar magnet is placed parallel to the bottom arm of the circuit, the frame begins to turn until it is at right angles to the magnet. The circuit's double loop prevents it from turning in the Earth's magnetic field, since the currents cancel out. The magnet, however, acts mainly on the arm nearest to it.

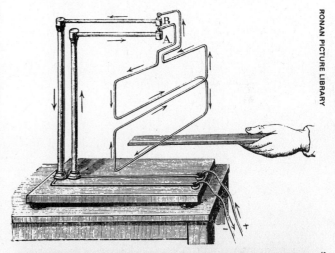

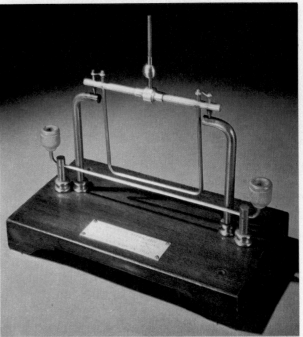

AMPHIBIOUS VEHICLES

Amphibious vehicles, or amphibians, can move both on land and in water under their own power. Development of amphibians for military and pleasure use has produced many different technical approaches, from the military DUKW to the American home made swamp buggies.

There are few details known of the first recorded powered amphibious vehicle. In 1805 a steam dredger named *Orukter Amphibolos* was built by the inventive American engineer Oliver Evans for the city of Philadelphia's docks. Theoretically it could motor overland from site to site, but there is no evidence that it ever did so.

The first true amphibious vehicle was probably the French Fournier of 1906, which combined a boat-type hull with an automobile chassis. A shaft transmission drove both the rear axle and a single propeller. Modern pleasure amphibians still follow this basic pattern.

Military types Most famous of all amphibians, and still one of the most versatile vehicles in use, is the American built General Motors Corporation DUKW ('Duplex Universal Karrier, Wheeled'), first built in 1942 and primarily used for ship-to-shore transport. Based on a truck chassis, it has a six cylinder 4.4 litre engine. All six wheels, which have rubber tyres, are driven.

The wheels all steer on land, and on water they assist a rudder. A single propeller is driven through a transfer case — a gearbox which enables it to be switched in and out. The six and a half ton amphibian can achieve 50 mile/h (80 km/h) on land and 6 mile/h (10 km/h) on water. Production ceased in 1945, but 'ducks' are still in use with armed forces all over the world.

Below: testing a Churchill Mark IV tank in water during World War 2. Such tanks were adapted for amphibious use by the addition of buoyancy chambers or a snorkel device.

Centre top: DUKWs massing by the Rhine before the assault crossing on 20 March 1945.

Centre bottom, far right top: tracked landing vehicles (LVTs) coming ashore during operation Deep Furrow, Mediterranean, 1971. These vehicles, about 30 ft (10 m) long, 12 ft (4 m) wide and 10 ft (3 m) high, can carry between 25 and 30 people and weigh about 38 tons (38,500 kg) when fully laden.

Far right bottom: control centre of the amphibious command ship USS Mount Whitney. This ship is a post World War 2 design. Amphibious assault ships within its command can carry up to 1500 troops plus amphibious vehicles, aircraft, helicopters and missiles.

Another major class of amphibian is known in the US as the LVT, short for Landing Vehicle, Tracked. The LVT, nicknamed the 'Buffalo', started as a rescue vehicle. It was designed in 1932 by Donald Roebling for use in the Florida swamplands and later developed as a military vehicle for carrying men and materials over rivers or on sea-borne landings.

The LVT is driven on both land and water by tracks equipped with W shaped protruberances (grousers) to give greater thrust. Buffers set between the driving wheels support the tracks and prevent them from being forced inwards by water pressure. This gives a greater effective driving surface.

Later models were fitted with Cadillac engines and automatic gearboxes. Current LVTs have side screens along the top run of the tracks and a cowl over the front of them, so that water carried forward by the top of the tracks is directed towards the rear again and so contributes to the forward thrust. Another gain in thrust comes from grilles at the back which channel the wash straight behind the vehicle. LVTs can cope with rocky beaches and heavy surf with equal ease.

During the Second World War, it was often necessary to convert a military vehicle into an amphibian, and Duplex Drive was devised by Nicholas Straussler to allow tanks to float into battle. The DD Sherman was so used on D Day in 1944. A platform of mild steel is welded round the water-proofed tank's hull and a raised canvas or plastic screen is erected round it to give buoyancy. This is generally supported by a series of rubber tubes inflated from cylinders of compressed air carried on the tank's superstructure.

Small propellers were originally driven by the tracks on early models, but the vulnerability of propellers on land led

to the increasingly widespread use of water jet propulsion. A ducted propeller sucks in water from under the body and squirts it through steering valves at the back. Russia leads in this field, but the armies of many nations now have troop carriers and reconnaissance vehicles driven by water jets.

Flotation screens are still used on a few military vehicles like the Vickers 37 ton tank and the Ferret Mk V Scout car, but most modern designers prefer either to forget all about temporary amphibious qualities or to build their tanks as true amphibians.

Developments in armour construction enable modern tanks to be lighter than their predecessors but just as well protected, so it is not difficult to produce light tanks that can float unassisted. A prime example is the Russian PT-76 amphibious tank, powered by a water jet.

The standard Russian technique allows tanks to submerge to cross rivers. This type of amphibian was pioneered during World War 2 by the Americans and Germans, and submersible tanks were to have been used in Hitler's abortive invasion of Britain.

They have snorkels (air tubes) extending to the surface, bringing air to both crew and engine. The French AMX30 tank has a 15 ft (4.6 m) long tube, wide enough to allow the commander to stand in the top and relay instructions to his submerged crew.

The air tube principle was also used on the British Austin Champ jeep. It had an extendable air pipe leading to the carburettor on the waterproofed engine. True amphibious jeeps were the World War 2 Volkswagen Schwimmwagen and the GPA ('General Purpose Amphibious') version of the

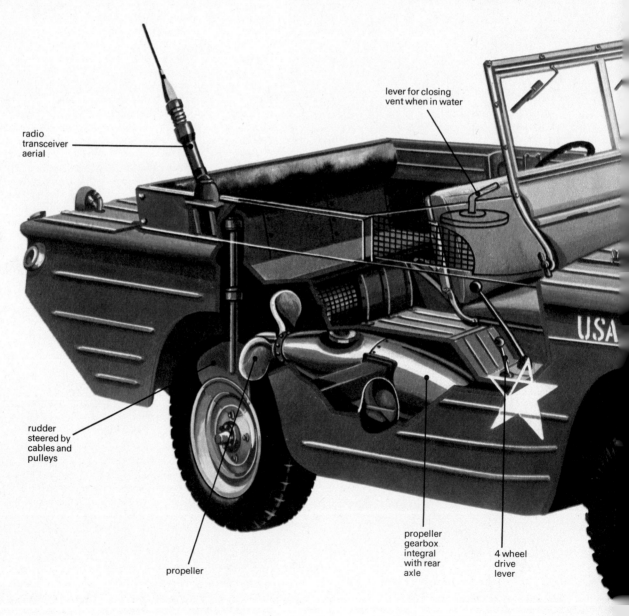

radio transceiver aerial

lever for closing vent when in water

USA

rudder steered by cables and pulleys

propeller

propeller gearbox integral with rear axle

4 wheel drive lever

American Jeep, which is still popular.

On the GPA Jeep, the watertight hull was constructed separately from the basic chassis to make replacement easy. The propeller was countersunk for protection, and was driven by a separate shaft mounted alongside the main drive to the rear wheels. It weighed more than a conventional Jeep, but could still reach 50 mile/h (80 km/h) on the road.

Pleasure vehicles Amphibians have also been developed for pleasure use, such as the German Amphicar, made from 1960 to 1967. This was an apparently normal small convertible which could take to the water. Its rear-mounted engine drove the rear wheels on land and twin nylon screws in water through a combination gearset mounted on the main gearbox housing.

The tyres were low set in the water and acted as both buoyancy bags and keels. The hull was steel, with rubber watertight seals where the propeller and the axle shafts penetrated the skin — as with the majority of amphibians of all types. The front wheels acted as rudders.

'Cars that swim' like the Amphicar have fallen out of fashion and a recent British design has yet to find a commercial manufacturer. A prototype of this four wheel drive Hydrocar has achieved 95 mile/h (153 km/h) on land and with its chain-driven wheels retracted 30 knots (56 km/h) through water.

It is driven in water by a 10 inch (25 cm) wide water jet. The hull is designed to turn the two bow waves inwards and form two rotating spirals on which the vehicle rides, thus minimizing waves and wash and increasing drive efficiency.

The current trend in pleasure amphibians is towards All

KEN LEWIS

engine cover

air intake to radiator

spray shield folds back on land

3426·S

exhaust outlet

The ¼ ton 4×4 Model GPA Amphibian was an amphibious version of the familiar Jeep, and was in use during World War 2. It was a rather hasty and makeshift conversion, and consisted of the original Jeep chassis and most of its mechanical parts, substantially unaltered and fitted with a watertight boat hull in place of the usual bodywork. Note the original Jeep seats and folding windshield. The modifications included adding a propeller and gearing to drive it to the back axle; the propeller was recessed into a U-shaped tunnel in the bottom of the hull to keep it from grounding when the Jeep was on land. There was also a rudder, which was turned by the steering wheel through an arrangement of cables and pulleys. The front wheels contributed to the steering effect in water; they could be switched in and out of four-wheel drive as on a normal Jeep. The spray shield on the nose was folded back to uncover the lights.

Terrain Vehicles (ATVs). Mostly American and Canadian built, they are usually based on two essential components: fat, ribbed tyres at very low pressures, and a transmission system using belts and tapered pulleys that adjust the speed automatically according to the throttle response.

The softness of the tyre, with pressures as low as 1.5 psi (0.1 bar), about one-fifteenth normal, lets the tread spread out to give maximum traction on land. The variable transmission relieves the driver of changing gear in normal forward use. Conventional gears are used for reverse, and in some cases to give high and low speed ranges too. From the transmission onwards the mechanical principles are the same on most ATVs — an output pulley is mounted on a cross-shaft terminating at either end in clutch plates which transmit the drive to the wheels on either side of the vehicle. To steer the vehicle, one of the clutches on these drive shafts is disengaged and comes in contact with a disc brake to slow down the wheels on one side.

Most ATVs have six or eight wheels, which steer and drive them in water as well as on land. The vehicles' light weight and low centre of gravity enable them to climb steep slopes easily and safely and the big soft tyres bend easily round obstacles. Engines are usually single cylinder units of around 250 cm³.

A typical ATV is the American Amphicat. It has a tough lightweight plastic body and is powered by a Curtis-Wright single cylinder two stroke air cooled engine. It has an expanding pulley and chain transmission with the additional refinement of a high, low and reverse range gearbox. A six wheeler, it weighs 396 pounds (180 kg) and can carry 480 pounds (220 kg).

Some ATVs have an articulated body, consisting of two separate watertight hulls that can move independently of each other in response to the terrain to keep all the wheels constantly in contact with the ground. The American Twister is such a vehicle. Others have rubber tracks.

The problems of travel in the Everglades swamps of Florida have led to the development of another type of amphibian, the swamp buggy.

Swamp buggies ride on large truck, tractor or aircraft tyres which support and drive them through thick mud and water.

More eccentric attempts at amphibians include an amphibious bicycle, shown at Lyons, France, in 1909. The front fork was linked by a rod to a rudder, and a small friction wheel at the rear drove a propeller. Cylindrical floats attached to the frame could be raised for land use.

There have been several attempts at converting ordinary road vehicles into temporary amphibians. A current one, built in New Zealand, consists of a floating platform onto which a car or lorry is driven. The front wheels hang through slots into the water and act as rudders. The driving wheels rest on rubber covered rollers which power twin propellers through a friction drive mechanism. Reverse gear provides a brake. Other similar devices have used simple rear mounted paddles.

The advance of the AIR CUSHION VEHICLE is reducing military demand for 'old fashioned' amphibians. Amphibians waste time when transferring from water to land and vice versa because the majority have to pause while the switch is made to another propulsion method. Indeed, there are very few amphibians with good performance on both land and water. But 'fun' amphibians, particularly ATVs, are becoming popular and their simplicity of design is making them increasingly attractive to the home builder.

Below: a British Army M2 amphibious bridging rig on manoeuvres in West Germany. These rigs have stacked decking which is lifted across by the gantry and coupled together to form a section of the bridge.

AMPLIFIER

An amplifier is a device for increasing the strength of a weak signal fed into it. Electronic amplifiers, which are the best known and most important type, are used in a huge variety of devices such as RADIO and TELEVISION receivers, RECORD PLAYERS, TAPE RECORDERS and HI-FI SYSTEMS, RADAR, analogue COMPUTERS, SERVOMECHANISMS and electronic equipment generally. Other devices which amplify in a different way include mechanical amplifiers such as the PANTOGRAPH, which enlarges drawings, hydraulic amplifiers such as the POWER BRAKES of a car, acoustic amplifiers such as the horn of an old fashioned gramophone [phonograph], the fluid amplifiers used in FLUIDICS and magnetic amplifiers, used as theatre light dimmers and in computers.

All electronic amplifiers work in much the same way, though they differ widely in design and in the *gain* (degree of amplification) they produce. Gain can be measured as a proportional increase in voltage (the usual method for amplifiers), in current or in wattage—total electrical power.

The heart of an amplifier, and the device that actually does the amplifying, is either a thermionic VALVE [vacuum tube] or a TRANSISTOR. Nearly all electronic amplifiers have several of these plus a set of RESISTORS, CAPACITORS, POTENTIOMETERS and related devices to control the flow of electricity through the basic amplifying components.

Valves [tubes] and transistors use different principles to perform the same function. Basically, they act as variable switches where the flow of a small current through one part of the device controls the flow of a larger current through another part. When the small current flows, the large current, which is drawn from a separate power source, flows too. When the small current stops flowing, the large one is shut off, and when the small current flows at, say, half power, so does the large one.

The proportion of the smaller current to the larger one is constant (at least in a linear amplifier, the most usual type). So if the small current is modulated (varied) by adding a signal from a record, tape or other source, the signal will be reproduced more or less faithfully at a much higher power in the form of a modulation of the large current. This large current can then be fed to a loudspeaker to convert it into an intelligible sound (or elsewhere, depending on what the amplifier is used for).

In the case of a transistor, the small current is fed in between the terminals known as the emitter and the base, and the large current flows between the emitter and the collector. So a transistor has only three terminals, not four, to carry the ingoings and outgoings of two currents. The collector,

Right top: a diagrammatical representation of a simple amplifier circuit. The signal voltage to be amplified is fed in from the left to the base-emitter circuit. The amplified signal voltage is found across the 'load' resistor at the top right of the diagram. The batteries B1 and B2 are required to provide the correct DC currents for the transistor to work. The battery B2 also provides the power source to produce the amplified signal across the load resistor.

Right centre and below: an artists's impression of how the above circuit works. When the current to the transistor base-emitter circuit is large, the collector-emitter circuit current is correspondingly larger. When the emitter-base current is small, the collector-emitter current is correspondingly smaller. The input signal is always fed to the base-emitter circuit, and the output from the collector-emitter circuit.

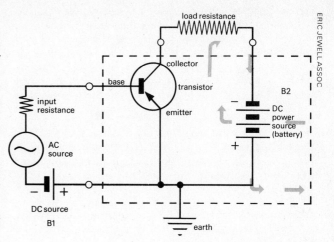

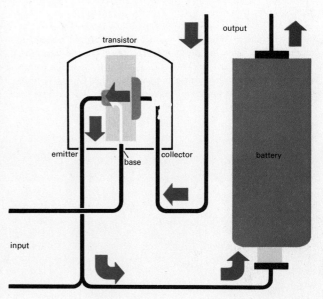

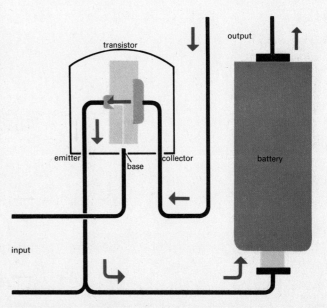

emitter and base are represented in the thermionic valve by the cathode, anode and grid. The names and principles are different, but the function is the same.

Amplifiers in practice

A simple amplifier as described would not normally produce enough gain for practical purposes. It might reach a 30 times increase in voltage. But an ordinary hi-fi amplifier operating in normal conditions would probably give a 100,000 times voltage increase. Some amplifiers used for other purposes have much higher gains than this.

Gains of this degree are produced by using an amplifier consisting of several stages. The output of the first stage is passed to the second stage and amplified further, and so on through as many stages as are needed to yield the necessary gain.

A hi-fi amplifier usually consists of two stages, the first a pre-amplifier with a fixed gain setting which boosts the incoming signal from the record, tape or radio to a manageable level at which it can be handled by the second stage, or main amplifier, which provides sufficient power to drive the speakers. This stage includes a volume control to adjust the final gain.

Amplifiers are normally designed with an inbuilt gain much higher than is actually needed or used. This is then moderated by the use of negative FEEDBACK, where a portion of the output signal is fed back to the input with a reversed polarity (current direction) to reduce the gain. In this way, the volume can be controlled by varying the amount of negative feedback. More importantly, distortion will be reduced and any changes in the supply voltage or the electronic components will have less effect on the gain.

If positive feedback were used, part of the output signal being fed back to the input with the *same* polarity to *boost* the gain, the result would probably be to produce unwanted oscillations, which are sometimes heard in public address systems as a loud howling noise. This is caused by the output boosting the input, the input increasing the output accordingly, the increased output further boosting the input, and so on up to uncontrollable levels, causing the amplifier to stop working. In public address systems this is caused by sound from the loudspeakers (the output end) reaching the microphone (the input end).

The quality of a linear amplifier is assessed by its ability to magnify the input signal 'faithfully', that is, without altering its essential shape. But amplifiers, like other physical systems, are not perfect. To give a faithful reproduction of, say, a musical instrument, an amplifier must respond to all the frequencies (pitches of sound) that the instrument produces, giving an equal response to all of them. In practice, this means that a hi-fi amplifier must respond equally to the whole range of audible frequencies, from about 30 Hz to 18 kHz (30–18,000 cycles per second). This range of frequency response is known as the bandwidth.

No actual amplifier can live up to this ideal, but high quality hi-fi amplifiers come closest. The frequency response can be partially altered by adjusting the treble and bass controls.

The video amplifiers used to form the pictures of TV and radar receivers have an enormous frequency bandwidth from 0 Hz (that is, direct current) to 6 MHz (6,000,000 cycles per second).

Amplifiers also suffer from harmonic distortion—output at frequencies twice, three or more times that of the signal—and from amplifier noise, a random jumble of different frequencies independent of the input signal. This is termed 'white noise'

because it includes all frequencies just as white LIGHT includes light waves of all frequencies between red and violet.

Amplifier noise can never be totally eliminated. It can always be heard in a sound amplifier as a slight hiss. But a good hi-fi amplifier can have a signal to noise ratio better than 3,000,000 to 1. For a 10 watt amplifier this would mean a noise power of less than 3 microwatts.

AMPLITUDE (see sine wave)

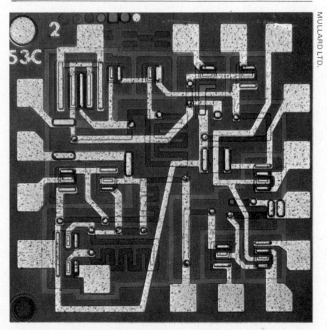

Above: an integrated circuit contains all the components of an amplifier stage, built into a silicon chip which may be as little as 0.2 inches (0.5) cm square and 0.01 inches (0.025 cm) thick. The input and output connections of the circuit are made to the square terminals around the edges of the chip.

Below: an electric guitar amplifier using valves [tubes] for its amplification stages, shown with its casing removed. The large square component on the left is the mains transformer, which reduces the mains voltage to that used by the valves. The output transformer, on the right, feeds the signal from the output stage of the amplifier to the loudspeaker terminals.

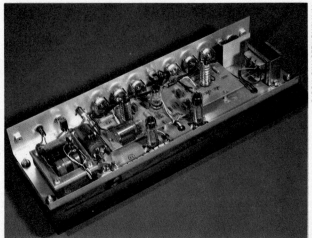

AM (amplitude modulation) RADIO

AM radio is the accepted name for the system of sound RADIO broadcasting used in the medium wave band in all parts of the world and in the long wave band in certain areas, notably Europe. The letters AM stand for *amplitude modulation*, the technique by which speech and music are impressed on the radio waves. The sound waves from the studio are converted into electrical signals by the microphones, and these electrical signals are used to vary the *amplitude*—the distance from 'peak' to 'trough' of the radio *carrier wave* generated at a constant frequency in the transmitting station. As a result, the signal radiated by the station varies in amplitude in step with the variations in the loudness and pitch of the sound in the studio. In the receiver, the amplitude variations of the radio signal are separated from the carrier wave by a process known as demodulation, and after further amplification are fed to the loudspeaker.

Amplitude modulation is also used by international broadcasting stations operating in the short wave band, and for some professional communications such as air traffic control, ship-to-shore traffic, and some mobile radio services.

AM radio stations in the medium wave band can provide a service over an area the size of a town or of a whole continent, depending upon the power of the transmitter which can vary from less than a hundred watts to hundreds of kilowatts. Long wave AM radio stations cover even larger areas. Normally, all radio waves travel only in straight lines, which would limit a radio station to an area of only about 40 miles (65 km) in diameter—as far as the horizon. Medium and long wave stations can actually cover much larger areas because their signals are bent round the curvature of the Earth by the ionosphere (an electrically charged layer in the upper atmosphere which can reflect radio waves).

In the US, where AM radio stations are operated on a commercial basis, coverage is generally and deliberately limited to one city and its environs. Major cities such as New York are served by large numbers of stations, each radiating a different programme.

In the UK, where until recently sound broadcasting was run entirely by the BBC, which is a public corporation, the emphasis has always been on nationwide coverage. This is achieved by distributing four programmes throughout the country over a cable network and broadcasting them from a large number of strategically placed transmitters each radiating the same programme or programmes. This pattern has now been altered by the establishment of medium wave local stations operated by both the BBC and the newly formed Independent Broadcasting Authority.

Use of AM

Amplitude modulation was the first technique to be used when broadcasting began in the US and Europe in the early 1920s. It proved highly successful but by the 1940s improvements in components and techniques were creating interest in the possibility of a very much higher sound quality in broadcasting.

The quality of reproduction on AM radio is not particularly good because of limitations in the amplitude modulation technique itself and because of overcrowding and subsequent interference in the medium wave band. Interference is particularly serious at night because the nature of the ionosphere alters after sunset, so that it can then reflect medium wave signals back to Earth a long way beyond their normal service area. Here, they interfere with other stations, producing whistles and other unwanted noises.

The AM method is still used for most popular broadcasting. Although the alternative FM RADIO system gives better quality, it is more difficult to receive, and is less suitable than AM for use in cheap transistor portables and car radios.

Recently, the rapidly falling cost of microcircuits (whole circuits on a single tiny chip of silicon) has made it possible to use in cheap transistor radios the highly complex circuits and techniques which previously could be employed only in expensive commercial receivers. One such technique, known as *single sideband*, will greatly reduce the interference effects that have long plagued AM reception. Single sideband will also provide better sound quality, particularly in areas near the limits of the area covered by a station, and will take up less channel space in the overcrowded medium wave band. Successful trials in the US have shown that a modification of this technique can provide a stereophonic AM radio service which will be particularly useful for reception in cars.

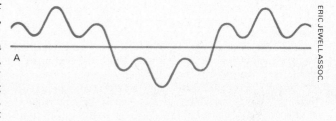

A

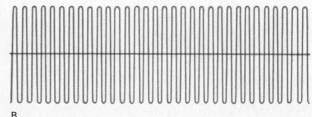

B

C

Above: how an AM signal is formed. The signal to be transmitted, typically a sound wave, is an irregular mixture of different frequencies (A). The carrier wave generated by the transmitter is a sinusoidal wave of a constant, much higher, frequency and, when no signal wave is superimposed on it, of constant amplitude (B). The complete AM signal is produced by combining the two waves so that the amplitude of the carrier is constantly modified by the amplitude of the signal (C). A radio receiver separates the two signals to recover the original sound wave.

ANAESTHETIC MACHINES

The anaesthetic machine is designed to induce a temporary state of unconsciousness in a patient, both making him insensitive to pain and reducing muscular reflexes sufficiently to allow surgery.

The machine supplies the patient's lungs with a mixture of anaesthetic gases which are selected by the anaesthetist according to the degree of unconciousness required, the health or age of the patient, and the type of surgery being performed.

The gases *nitrous oxide* (N_2O) and *cyclopropane* (C_3H_6) are commonly used for inhalation anaesthesia, supplied together with oxygen (O_2).

Nitrous oxide is a non-flammable gas, compressed into a liquid and stored in cylinders. It is used as the sole anaesthetic agent in most dentistry. Because the gas is non-irritating to the lungs, it is often used to induce unconsciousness before introducing a more pungent anaesthetic such as ether.

Cyclopropane is stored as a liquid in low-pressure cylinders. It is extremely potent, highly explosive, and is used in concentrations of up to 20% in oxygen to induce anaesthesia.

Liquid anaesthetic agents, such as *ether* and *halothane* are widely used. To make them breathable, they must first be broken into droplets by a vaporizer. *Trichloroethylene* vapour is also used, but at a low concentration.

Design of machines

The most basic anaesthetic machine is Boyle's apparatus, introduced in 1917 and still very widely used, in a much improved form. The components are usually either supported on a movable trolley, or installed conveniently close to the operating table.

Gas is supplied from cylinders attached to the machine or by hoses from a bulk supply in another part of the hospital. In this case, the machine may have cylinders as a standby. The normal complement of cylinders is two oxygen (coloured black with a white top, for easy identification), two nitrous oxide (blue), one carbon dioxide (grey), and one small cylinder of cyclopropane (orange). Carbon dioxide (CO_2) is included as a stimulant, should breathing become weak.

Cylinders and hoses have connections of different designs to prevent attachment to the wrong inlet. Reducing valves are fitted to the high pressure O_2, CO_2 and N_2O cylinders to supply the gases at a suitably low pressure. Cyclopropane, however, is already at a very low pressure and is fed direct into the machine.

The selected gases are fed separately into flowmeters, to show the quantities of each present in the gas mixture. Flowmeters are tapered tubes, containing loosely fitting plungers. The plunger 'floats' on the gas as it passes through the tube, a more rapid flow being required to carry it to the top, where the tube is widest. The height of the plunger on a scale indicates the flow rate.

When vapour from liquid anaesthetics is to be added to the mixture, the combined gas flow is directed through a vaporizer. This is a container holding liquid ether, halothane, or trichloroethylene, which evaporates as the gas mixture is blown across the surface, or bubbled through it.

From the vaporizer, the mixture passes to a rubber reservoir bag. This fills with gas, then deflates as the patient inhales, refilling with fresh mixture while the patient exhales.

The final anaesthetic mixture passes along a wide corrugated rubber tube to the mask, which is held over the patient's face. An expiratory valve is fitted to the mask to prevent exhaled gases being forced back into the incoming mixture, which would cause CO_2 build-up and eventual suffocation. Exhaled gases leaving the expiratory valve are often ducted out of the operating theatre to reduce the risk of explosion.

A tube called a *pharyngeal airway* is often passed into the patient's throat to prevent the tongue from obstructing gas flow to the lungs. In the more complex 'closed circuit' systems, exhaled gases are not exhausted from the apparatus, but pass through a cylinder containing soda-lime (a mixture of sodium hydroxide and lime), which absorbs the carbon dioxide, then pass back into the reservoir bag, from which the mixture is re-breathed. This economises on the volume of gas used, but requires careful control to keep the proportions of the gas mixture constant.

If the patient's respiration is inhibited by deep anaesthesia, or by use of muscle-relaxant drugs, a *ventilator* may be used to assist breathing. This is a rubber bellows which pumps the gas mixture into the lungs automatically, the patient exhaling normally. Blood pressure, pulse rate and various other factors may also be monitored on instruments attached to the machine, where they can be conveniently read by the anaesthetist.

Less elaborate machines are used in dental anaesthesia, where a simple mixture of N_2O and O_2 is generally sufficient for the degree of anaesthesia required.

Simpler still are 'gas and air' machines used for the relief of pain rather than anaesthesia, for example in childbirth. The gas and air are supplied ready-mixed in the correct proportions, so the patient can usually operate the machine herself.

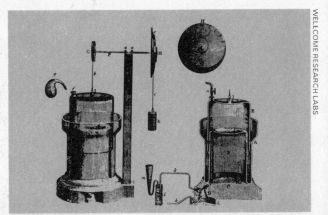

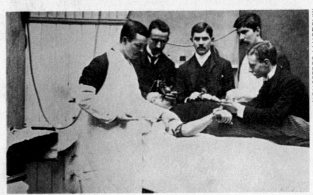

Top: Sir Humphry Davy's gas machine of 1800. Davy was one of the first to experiment with nitrous oxide (laughing gas) as an anaesthetic. Above: an operation at the Royal Hospital, Belfast in 1885 using ether. Ether was probably the first anaesthetic used in surgery.

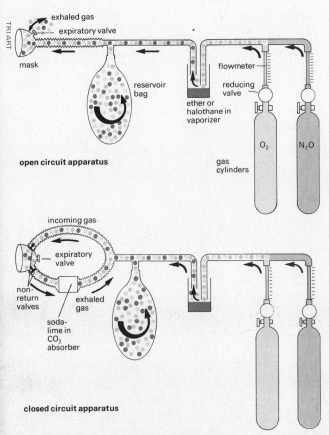

Above : a modern unit with pipelines and standby cylinders.
Below : the upper picture shows the 'open-circuit' or Boyle's apparatus
and the lower one shows the 'closed-circuit' or rebreathing apparatus.

open circuit apparatus

closed circuit apparatus

ANALYSIS, CHEMICAL

Daily in laboratories throughout the world many thousands of chemical analyses are performed. Almost every industry, and especially the CHEMICAL INDUSTRY itself, uses chemical analysis in the QUALITY CONTROL of both raw materials and finished products, many of which must meet exacting specifications. Other industries which are dependent on chemical analysis include OIL REFINING, FOOD PROCESSING, pharmaceuticals, PAPER MAKING, STEEL and metalworking. Added to these are medical laboratory tests, forensic medicine, government testing (such as analyses to see if toxic residues—for example pesticides or even lead—are present in foodstuffs or the water supply), and research projects carried out by industries and universities. Tests may range from the analysis of a geologist's rock sample, which may reveal that it is rich in a particular metal, to isolating and finding out the composition of a hormone such as insulin.

Sometimes in chemical analysis it is necessary to identify the ELEMENTS present (known as *qualitative analysis*) and, having established this, to find out their relative amounts (known as *quantitative analysis*). Most analyses, however, are aimed at finding out how much. Frequently in routine analyses, methods are developed to measure the amount of only one particular COMPOUND. This often involves freeing it from other chemical compounds present in the sample, which would interfere with the final procedure used to detect the compound in question. Some instruments, particularly the gas CHROMATOGRAPH, enable several compounds in a sample to be quantitatively determined at the same time.

The methods used for chemical analysis often depend on the size of the sample available. Tests involving chemical reactions with other substances are used for larger samples, while instruments, such as the gas chromatograph, are used for very small samples.

Elemental inorganic analysis
Given, say, a sample of soil, it would be possible to analyze it using the classical or 'wet' chemical methods of the school laboratory, which require a minimum of equipment, such as a standard set of bench reagents (hydrochloric acid, sulphuric acid, caustic soda, ammonium hydroxide), glassware, gas burners, an oven and a fume cupboard with a source of the gas hydrogen sulphide. The first step is to try dissolving the sample in water. Part or all of it may be soluble in water. Should this fail, various reagents, both acid and alkaline, are tried. If these do not dissolve the sample it will be necessary to use a *flux*. This is a solid, or a mixture of solids, which when mixed with the sample and heated in a crucible may react giving soluble products.

The chemical elements to be identified are now in a convenient form for analysis because in solution they will be IONS, or atoms or groups of atoms carrying electric charges. In their ionized state elements undergo various chemical reactions, which by process of elimination can be used to identify them.

Systematic separation of metals
This type of analysis is generally followed by advanced chemistry classes in schools. It is possible to separate any or all of the twenty or so possible *cations* (positively charged ions) first into solubility groups, and then from each other within each group. Thus all metals that form insoluble chlorides are precipitated (solidified) out of solution as insoluble salts by adding hydrochloric acid. The precipitate (solid part) is filtered off and forms the first group, while the remaining

groups are in the filtrate (liquid part), to which the next group-reagent is added, and so on.

In the best known separation scheme the consecutive group-reagents and the precipitates they produce are: hydrochloric acid—chlorides; gaseous hydrogen sulphide bubbled through acidified solution—acid-insoluble sulphides; ammonia—hydroxides; ammonium sulphide in alkaline solution—acid soluble sulphides; ammonium carbonate—carbonates. The metals remaining in the filtrate after that form the last solubility group.

Each precipitate can be dissolved again and individual metals within the group separated by precipitation with reagents or by other means. For example, the insoluble carbonates of calcium (Ca), strontium (Sr), and barium (Ba) can be dissolved in acid, and when potassium chromate is added to this solution only barium chromate is precipitated, leaving the calcium and strontium salts in solution. Alternatively, the presence of a metal can be detected by a specific reaction, if this is not affected by the presence of other metals.

Tests for acid radicals The number of possible *anions* (negative ions) is much larger than that of the possible cations. Most anions, however, can undergo reactions other than precipitation ones, and many of these can be used as specific tests for the presence of individual anions. The iodide ion, I^-, for example, can be oxidized by potassium nitrate to iodine, which gives a characteristic blue colour when mixed with a starch solution. But no widely accepted scheme for the separation of all anions exists.

Gravimetric determinations Gravimetric methods use a suitable chemical reaction to produce a product which is then weighed. Once the qualitative composition of a sample is known, a way in which to separate and determine the amount of any particular component can be devised. For example, barium can be estimated as the insoluble sulphate. To ensure that all the particles of the barium sulphate precipitate are large enough to be retained during filtering and washing, only a small excess of the acid is used, and the precipitate is digested—that is, left in its 'mother' liquor for a time—to allow larger crystals of precipitate to grow. The precipitate is then filtered, washed (to remove traces of acid), dried, cooled, and weighed to constant weight.

After checking that further drying and cooling does not

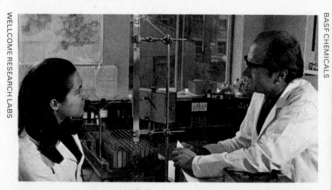

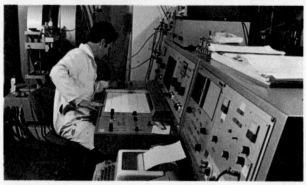

Top: gel filtration using dextran gel, a complex carbohydrate which acts as a sieve in reverse, retaining small molecules and allowing large ones to pass through faster. Here a blood protein (an antibody) is being separated from other molecules, seen as dyed bands on the column. The antibody passes through first, is collected and used to detect a wide variety of bacterial and viral infections in body tissue.

Below: nuclear magnetic resonance provides more structural information about molecules than any other technique. Organic molecules placed in a powerful magnetic field absorb radio frequencies. The intensity and frequency of the signals can give detailed information on the structure of a molecule. Modern on-line computer methods increase the versatility and sensitivity. It is used for finding details of therapeutic drugs and analyzing tiny amounts of breakdown products.

produce any change in weight, the weight is divided by the formula-weight (the total weight of each atom in a compound or molecule) of the precipitate, and multiplied by the weight of the relevant constituent in the formula (in this case barium).

Titrations A much faster way of determining the quantity of a substance is by measuring the exact volume of a *standard solution* (one which contains a known amount of a particular chemical) of a reagent that has reacted completely with a measured volume of a solution containing the sample. This is called a titration and is widely used as an analytical method. The solution containing the substance of which the quantity is to be determined is diluted to an exact volume (usually one litre) from which known sample portions, say, 50 millilitre portions, can then be measured out into a conical flask. Measured quantities of a standard solution are run into the conical flask until the exact equivalence or end point (that is the point at which equivalent amounts of the unknown and the standard substance have reacted) is reached, and the volume of standard solution used read off.

The end point of a neutralization reaction may be detected by observing a change of colour of a suitable acid-base indicator such as phenolphthalein, which changes from colourless to pink in the presence of an alkali. For other types of reaction such as precipitation or OXIDATION-REDUCTION, it is often possible to detect a tiny excess of the reagent. So, when oxidizing with a standard iodine solution from a *burette*, starch can be used as an indicator, as it gives a blue colour with the slightest excess of the iodine.

The normality—the strength—of the standard solution multiplied by the volume used gives the amount of the substance in the sample portion.

Gas analysis Volumetric analysis of a mixture of gases consists of measuring its volumes at known temperature and pressure, absorbing one of its constituent gases in a suitable reagent, measuring the remaining volume, absorbing the next constituent, and so on. Some of the reagents used and the gases they absorb are: pyrogallol (trihydroxybenzene) for oxygen, caustic potash for carbon dioxide, a cuprous salt for carbon monoxide, and bromine as a bromide solution for unsaturated HYDROCARBONS such as ethylene.

The quantity of a gas can also be determined by other methods such as by measuring the increase in weight of an

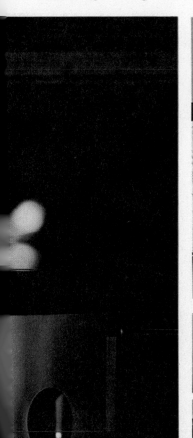

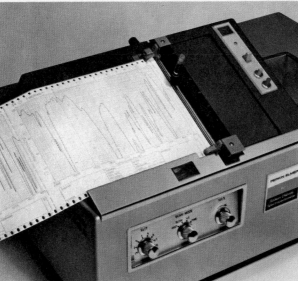

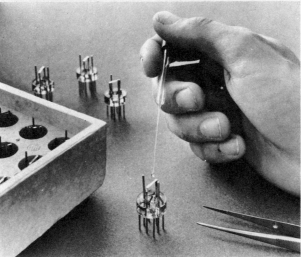

PERKIN GLUES

U.K. ATOMIC ENERGY AUTHORITY

Far left: optical phenomena are useful aids in the hands of the analytical chemist to find the purity of organic compounds.

Shown here is an atomic absorption spectrophotometer. The sample is vaporized in a flame and the spectrum which is characteristic to that particular compound is recorded immediately as a direct print-out.

Top left: this spectrophotometer measures the amount of infra-red light absorbed by a substance over a range of wavelengths.

Since glass and quartz both absorb infra-red light, the optics have to be made of rock salt, sodium chloride. Liquid paraffin is used to dissolve the samples, which are held in cells with rock salt windows.

Bottom left: mass spectrometric analysis using radioactive isotopic tracers for each of the elements to be determined in a sample is a very sensitive technique. A known quantity of tracer for each element to be measured is added to the sample solution, a drop of which is being transferred to the filament of the mass spectrometer source unit. It is then heated to dryness before being placed in the instrument.

absorbent, by absorption in a known quantity of a reagent followed by titration to determine how much of the reagent is left unchanged (this is used for sulphur dioxide, SO_2), or indirectly using a chemical reaction to produce another substance, which is then determined quantitatively.

Electrical methods The scope and accuracy of classical analysis can be increased by electrical methods. ELECTROLYSIS, where the metal is deposited on an inert (for example, platinum) electrode, is one of the methods of gravimetric analysis. Titration end points can be detected by the properties of the sample solution, for example, by monitoring the pH (the acidity or alkalinity of a substance), the oxidation potential (its ability to oxidize substances), or the electrical conductivity.

Some electrical methods, however, stand quite apart from classical analysis. One of these is polarography, a process based on electrolysis. An electric current is passed through a solution of the substance to be analyzed. Its voltage is gradually increased at a steady rate until *decomposition potential* is reached—a 'breakthrough' point at which the solution suddenly becomes much more conductive and the current flowing

through it increases. After a while, however, *polarization* occurs: the electrodes which pass current to the solution are covered in a non-conductive layer of substances released by the electrolysis and the current flow drops. Plotting on a graph the rate at which these changes occur allows many elements to be identified.

Organic analysis Organic analysis deals with organic compounds, the often complex carbon compounds which are mainly found in living matter. It is seldom concerned with identifying pure elements by themselves.

Different organic compounds can usually be separated from each other and from inorganic compounds by physical methods. DISTILLATION is one way to separate compounds with different boiling points, sometimes carried out under reduced pressure, which reduces the boiling point. Steam distillation, in which a sample is boiled in water so that some of the volatile compounds distil over with the steam, is a good way to extract essential oils. Solvent extraction is sometimes useful because some compounds are soluble in a particular solvent, while others are not. Chromatography is another separation technique in which components can be selectively

Above: the lamp determination of sulphur in volatile petroleum products such as diesel fuel is important for the quality control of refined products, which must often meet stringent regulations. The sample is burned and the sulphur measured as sulphur dioxide.

Above right: automatic air sampling apparatus is used to collect smoke samples from various UK and European cities. The sulphur dioxide content is determined by measuring the sulphur present using nephelometry. Light is passed through the sample (in this case barium sulphate) and its dispersion compared with that of standard solutions.

Below right: a sample of lubricating oil used for the lubrication of marine diesel engines is undergoing titration to determine its alkalinity. Analysis of marine oils during service is vital to ships.

AN ESSO PHOTO

AN ESSO PHOTO

SHELL LABS, AMSTERDAM

removed from a mixture.

Once an organic compound is separated from others and purified by one or more of the above methods, it can be analyzed both qualitatively and quantitatively. Both these stages consist essentially of breaking up the organic compound into inorganic substances by such means as heating it in a stream of gas or with a reagent, and then analyzing the inorganic products. To obtain the molecular formula, that is the actual number of atoms of each element in the MOLECULE, the molecular weight is needed. This is often obtained by mixing the compound with camphor and measuring the melting point of the mixture. Many further tests are often needed before the structural formula, and hence the identity of the compound, can be found.

Identification of the more common organic compounds is usually achieved by much simpler means. Whether or not they are soluble in water, ether, acids, and bases narrows down the possibilities. General tests, known as class reactions, reveal the presence of functional groups of atoms, such as CARBOXYLIC (-COOH), keto (-CO) or primary ALCOHOL (-CH$_2$OH). Once the functional groups of a compound are known,

derivatives may be prepared, and their melting (or boiling) points measured. If the melting points of two different derivatives of the compound agree with those of the corresponding derivatives of a known compound, this generally indicates that the known and unknown are identical.

Physical methods The identification of a substance can be assisted or confirmed by measuring its physical properties such as density, melting point, refractive index (see OPTICS), and the X-RAY diffraction pattern, which is useful for determining crystal structure. In addition, many physical measurements are used to detect and estimate specific chemical substances. The COLORIMETER is a useful instrument for the quantitative analysis of substances which react with a specific reagent to produce a colour. A graph is produced using a set of standards where the colour intensities correspond to known amounts of a particular substance. The colour intensity of the unknown sample is measured and the amount present estimated from the graph.

Other methods used include the various SPECTROSCOPIC techniques (emission and atomic absorption), MASS SPEC-TROSCOPY and POLARIMETRY.

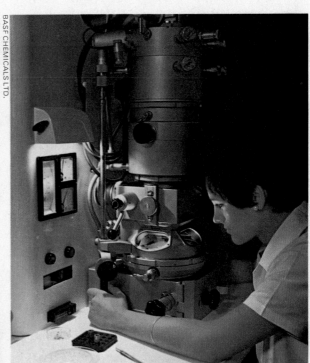

Above: a research chemist uses an electron microscope to obtain detailed information about the structure of new dyes. This instrument provides enormously magnified pictures. A beam of electrons from an electron gun is used to illuminate the object. The sample is in the form of a very thin film. The image is received on a fluorescent screen and photographed.

Left top: colorimetric methods are often used in chemical analysis to find the amount of a particular element present in a sample. After the element has reacted with a colouring agent, the intensity of the colour produced is measured to find the quantity present.

Left bottom: gravimetric analysis is one of the oldest techniques for finding the amount of a particular element in a sample. The element is isolated by preparing an insoluble compound which is weighed.

ANCHOR

An anchor moors a vessel to the sea bed, generally by a combination of its own weight and by hooking itself into the bottom. A typical anchor is shaped so that a horizontal pull causes it to dig itself in firmly, but an upward pull dislodges it easily. It is attached to the vessel by a cable—this is a heavy chain in large ships. The cable must lie flat for some distance along the sea bed if the anchor is to be effective, and the length of cable needed for this is from three to eight times the depth of water.

Unmooring, or 'weighing' the anchor, is carried out by winching in the cable. This pulls the vessel over the anchor's position, and when the cable is more or less vertical the anchor should dislodge.

The earliest anchors were simple stone weights: the *mudweight* is still used on inland waterways for cruising craft. Underwater archaeologists have found a large number of stone anchors of different shapes and sizes in the Mediterranean, some dating back at least to the Bronze Age. One of the most common types was a roughly triangular stone with a hole in the top corner for the cable. Sometimes there were holes in the bottom corners, perhaps for wooden *flukes* or digging ends. Some time after 1000 BC metal began to be used, with huge wooden anchors with lead *stocks* (crosspieces). Around this time the traditional fixed anchor evolved which was used well into the 19th century.

The flukes of this type of anchor are on arms which are set at right angles to the top crosspiece, or stock. If, when an anchor first touches the sea bottom, the stock is the first part to dig in, the anchor will tend to twist over when pulled so that a fluke is stuck in instead.

Large anchors of this type were rather unwieldy on board ship, so the stowing type was invented, which has a stock with one bent end. It is held in place by a metal key when being used, but can be folded flat along the length of the anchor for stowing. This type, sometimes called the Admiralty

anchor, is commonly found in yachts and other small craft.

The effectiveness of a type of anchor depends on the nature of the sea bed. The Admiralty anchor does not hold well on a soft bottom, since the digging area is fairly small. A variation which helped to overcome this is the Trotman's anchor, which has its flukes on pivoted arms to allow them to dig in at the most effective angle.

The anchor used on most large modern ships is the *stockless* anchor. The large flukes of this type are pivoted, and can

SONIA HALLIDAY

Above: this detail from a third century AD Roman mosaic at Dougga, Tunisia, can be seen in the Bardo Museum, Tunis. The anchor shown has no stock, and would have been difficult to secure unless the anchor man went underwater with it—only possible in shallow waters.

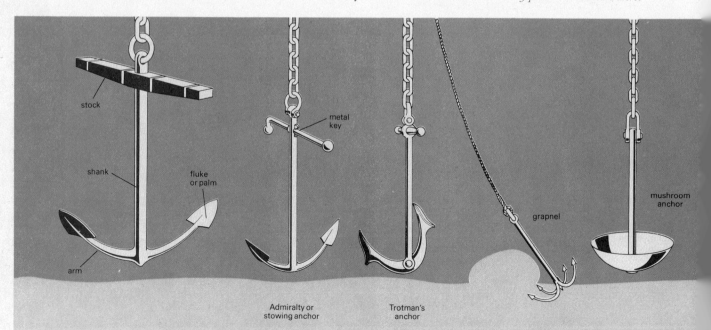

stock

shank

fluke or palm

arm

Admiralty or stowing anchor

metal key

Trotman's anchor

grapnel

mushroom anchor

move out from the anchor by a maximum of 45°. Projections on the flukes called *tripping palms* make sure that the flukes stick into the sea bed. A horizontal pull on the cable makes them dig in even more. As the device has no stock, it can be pulled up to the mouth of the hawse pipe until only the arms and flukes are protruding, so it is always ready for use.

One variation of this is the Danforth, which uses a small stock at the bottom of the anchor to stabilize it. Another, the CQR or plough anchor, has a single fluke shaped like a ploughshare, which digs itself deeper as more pull is applied.

Other forms of anchor include the *grapnel*, with four or five arms to snag in projections on the sea bed, which can also be used to drag for lost objects. The *mushroom* anchor has a shape which is ideal for permanently mooring lightships and dredgers to a soft sea bed. Its mushroom shape tends to sink deeply and hold in place by suction, though because this takes some time to happen a straightforward weight is often used for the purpose.

The *sea anchor* is a structure of wood and canvas shaped rather like a large sock. It is paid out over the bows of a vessel, and the drag brings the craft round so that it faces the direction of the oncoming waves. This is useful when a vessel is not under way in a heavy sea, for example. Small vessels may use similar devices, called *drogues*, from the stern to steady them when sailing with the wind in a heavy sea. In an emergency, a plastic bucket will often do the same job.

Below : a sequence showing types of anchors which have been used. Many other variations have been produced, such as the rond anchor. This has only one fluke and no stock, and is used for small craft on inland waterways—it is simply stuck into the bank by hand. At the right of this illustration can be seen the stockless anchor. When being lowered the flukes will fall to one side of the central position, as shown by the dotted lines. When a tripping palm touches the sea bed, the flukes will turn in the direction of pull, depicted by the first side view. As the drag becomes more horizontal, the flukes begin to dig well in.

ANEMOMETER

Anemometers are instruments for measuring wind speed, but their use has also been extended to the measurement of fluid velocities in general. There is a variety of anemometers available. The type used depends on the nature of the fluid, the range of velocities likely to be encountered and the accuracy required.

For the measurement of wind speeds, however, there are essentially three types of anemometer: the cup, propeller and Pitot-static pressure tube anemometer.

Cup anemometer The simplest type of wind speed indicator is the rotating cup anemometer. This consists of three or four conical or hemispherical cups mounted at the ends of horizontal spokes radiating from a vertical rotating shaft. The concave surfaces of the cups offer greater wind resistance than their convex surfaces, causing the cups to rotate in the wind.

In steady wind conditions, the cups attain a speed approaching that of the wind, so that the wind speed can be calculated by measuring the rate of rotation of the shaft. This can be determined by attaching a revolution counter to the shaft and counting the number of revolutions in a fixed time. A contact mechanism can also be attached to the shaft, providing an electrical pulse once every revolution. These pulses can be recorded, or counted, at a distance from the instrument.

Alternatively, a continuous indication of the rate of rotation (and hence, the wind speed) can be achieved by coupling to the shaft a small dynamo which produces a voltage output proportional to the rate of rotation. Wind speeds can then be read directly off a voltmeter suitably calibrated.

In gusty winds, the cup anemometer tends to overrate the average wind speed because the rotating cups tend to speed up faster than they slow down, and this can produce 'overrunning' errors as high as 30%. Nevertheless, it is a simple and inexpensive device capable of measuring wind speeds from 5 to 100 mile/h (8 to 160 km/h).

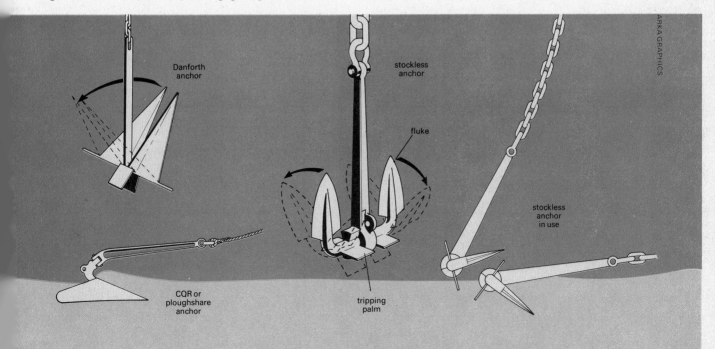

Danforth anchor

CQR or ploughshare anchor

stockless anchor

fluke

tripping palm

stockless anchor in use

ARKA GRAPHICS

Far left: Lind type anemometer made in 1876. This type was first made by Dr James Lind of Edinburgh in 1776. The U-tube holds water up to the zero marks on the scale, and the wind vane rotates the tube system so that the open end faces into the wind. From the difference of the liquid levels the velocity and pressure of the wind can be calculated from a table prepared for the instrument.

Near left: a portable anemometer made about 1900 by Jules Richard of Paris. As well as the counter shown, there is an electrical contact which is made every 2.5 metres run of the wind and is employed to operate a distant counter reading or a telephone. The vanes are set at 45° to allow for small changes in wind direction. The instrument registers winds as light as 0.1 metres/second.

Propeller anemometer

Propeller anemometers are suitable for the measurement of low air speeds in the region of 1 to 25 mile h (1.6 to 40 km/h). Here the blades of a propeller, or fan, are attached to a horizontal rotating shaft which is pointed into the wind by a tail fin like that of a weather vane. The speed of rotation is again proportional to the wind speed and can be measured by the same methods used on cup anemometers.

Mechanical anemometers cannot be accurately calibrated simply by knowing their dimensions, since factors such as friction vary from instrument to instrument. They must therefore be calibrated in the controlled conditions of a wind tunnel.

Pitot-static anemometer

The Pitot-static pressure tube anemometer is mechanically simple, having no moving parts, and has many applications including wind tunnel calibration and air speed indicators on aircraft.

The main part is a 'probe' consisting of two separate tubes aligned upstream. One tube (the PITOT tube) has its upstream end open, and air flowing into the open end causes pressure in it to build up. The pressure in this tube is the sum of the static pressure of the air (that is, the normal atmospheric pressure) and the dynamic pressure produced by the flow of air into the tube.

The other tube is the static tube, closed and rounded at its upstream end with a series of holes around the tube some distance downstream. As the airstream is effectively undisturbed by the rounded front of the static tube, the pressure inside this tube is therefore the static pressure alone.

The downstream ends of the two tubes are connected to a differential pressure gauge which measures the pressure difference between the two tubes, thus giving the dynamic pressure of the Pitot tube. Knowing the air density and the dynamic pressure enables the air speed to be determined.

Pitot-static anemometers create some disturbance in the air stream and so are not suitable for velocity measurements in confined spaces where such disturbances may be important. Furthermore, without special design, these devices are inaccurate at low air speeds. For such specialist applications as low air speeds, confined spaces and especially liquid velocity measurements, other types of FLOWMETERS such as hot-wire and laser anemometers become important.

ANTENNA (see aerial)

Above: modern cup type anemometers are used to estimate the total run of the wind as it passes an observation point during a specific period. The window is angled to assist reading when the instrument is above the observer. It is not feasible to calibrate a mechanical anemometer from its dimensions. Its performance has to be determined by observing it in a windtunnel whose airspeed is measured by a pressure anemometer.

revolving cups

revolution counter

mounting pole

ANTI-AIRCRAFT GUN

Anti-aircraft (AA) guns were first used in World War 1 (1914–1918) when they were adapted from equipment designed for other roles. Their job was to prevent enemy aircraft flying at such a height that they could observe, photograph, range artillery, bomb with accuracy or attack troops at low level; and they had to prevent hostile aircraft from flying in formation which allowed them to use the power of their combined defensive armament against counter-attacking aircraft. These requirements persisted until the end of World War 2, by which time the great speed of jet aircraft made AA gunnery impractical against high flying targets.

The AA problem   This may be summarized as 'the time of flight'. While the AA shell is travelling upwards towards the target aircraft, that target is itself travelling through the sky. For example, a target travelling at the now modest speed of 200 mph (320 km/h) would travel almost 1¾ miles (2.8 km) during the 30 second time of flight of a 3.7 inch AA shell. The position of the target is known at the moment the gun fires but once the shell starts on its way no further control can be exercised over it, and so certain assumptions must be made about the behaviour of the target during the time of flight of the projectile to meet it. These assumptions are that the target will maintain a constant course, height and speed shortly before and during the flight of the shell or, if any of these are changing, it will be at a constant rate. The higher and faster the aircraft is flying, the longer the time of flight of the shell and the less likely are the assumptions to be justified.

The apparatus that was developed to pinpoint the future position of the target was called a predictor. Although extremely complex in design, it was simple in principle. The predictor followed the path of the target and measured the bearing (direction) and elevation. The change in bearing and elevation in a short period of time enabled the course and speed to be calculated and this, with the height supplied by a modified range finder, gave all the target data. Initially an optical range finder was employed, but this could not be used at night and later was replaced by radar. The trajectory of the shell depended on its initial velocity, the retardation due to its shape and diameter, its weight and stability in flight, together with the meteorological conditions at various altitudes through which it passed. All these factors were fed into the predictor.

The likelihood of a direct hit was obviously very low so the high explosive filling of the shell was detonated by a time fuze set to function after the calculated time of flight for the shell to reach the target. The lethal radius of the bursting shell was sufficient to allow for some error in prediction. The automatic fuze setter received data from the predictor and set the fuze of the shell immediately before the automatic loader placed it in the chamber of the gun. If all was correct, the shell was sent on its way to intercept the target and either hit it or, if the fuze functioned correctly sufficiently closely, to destroy it by blast.

An improvement on the time fuze was the proximity fuze which enabled the fuze setting procedure to be omitted. The proximity fuze works by using a radio device built into the shell, to detect when it is near the target. The strength of the

One of the earliest forms of anti-aircraft defence, a machine gun mounted on a wooden post. This one is at an airfield in Germany during World War 1.

The United States 'Skysweeper' 75 mm anti-aircraft gun represents the final stage of development of the heavy gun before it was superseded by the missile. It was used during the last part of World War 2 and in Korea. The gun aimed itself automatically by radar and a computer. Loading was also mechanized, the automatic loader (shown on the right) taking rounds alternately from the left and right ammunition cylinders. Power was provided by an electric motor mounted above the barrel. The gun's recoil was reduced to a manageable level by the muzzle brake at the end of the barrel, a set of 'fingers' ridged on their inner surface so that they caught the slipstream of the shell and pulled the barrel forward. If the computer failed, the gun could still be aimed by eye from the seat. If the electric power failed too, it could be loaded manually and aimed by means of handwheels and the emergency sighting mechanism on the far side of the barrel.

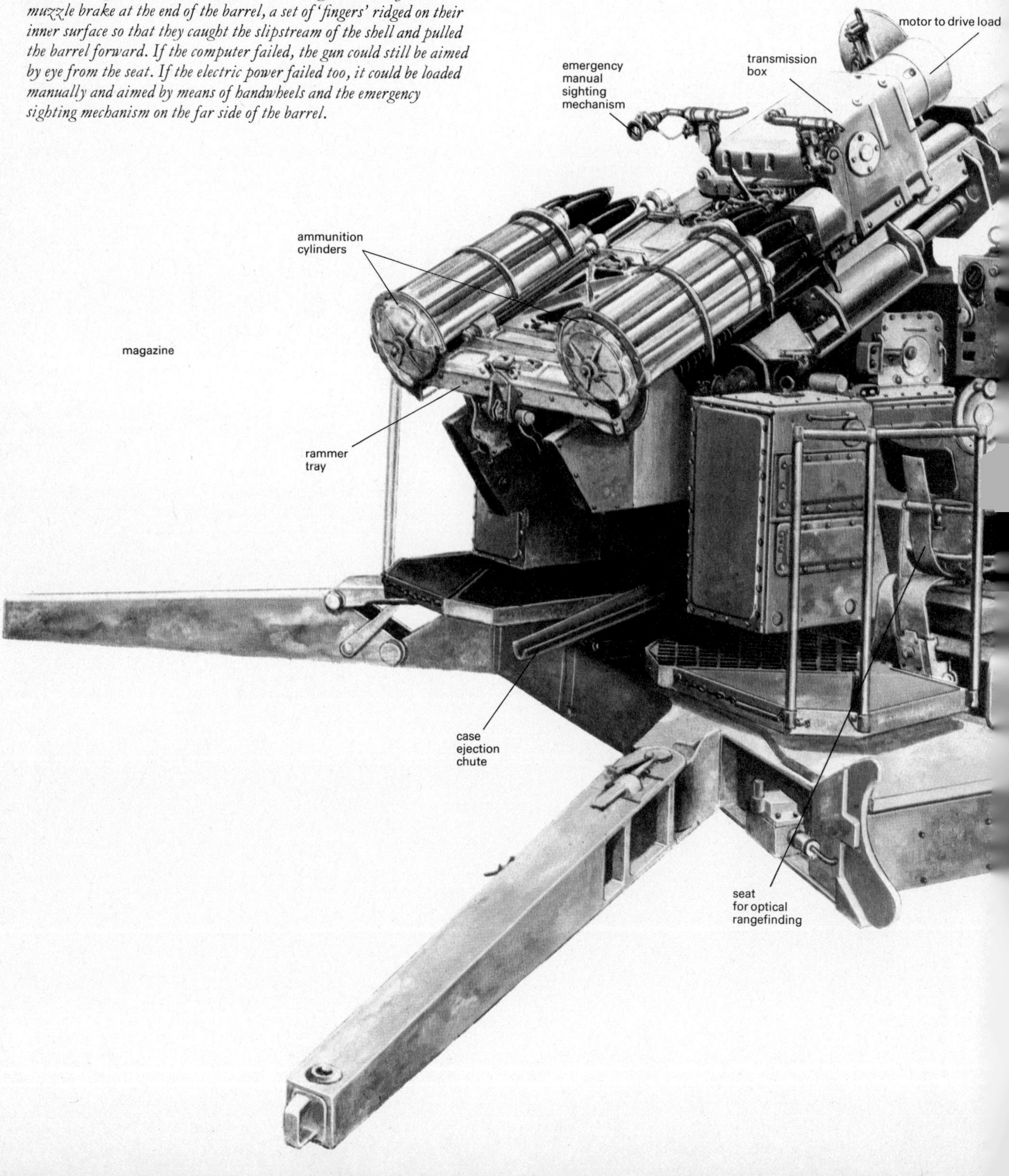

motor to drive load

transmission box

emergency manual sighting mechanism

ammunition cylinders

magazine

rammer tray

case ejection chute

seat for optical rangefinding

JOHN BATCHELOR

muzzle brake to control recoil

chanism

optical rangefinder

predictor computer

firing platform

ramming rolls

round

fuze

fuze jaws

round is fired

breechblock closes

case is ejected

Above right : the high rate of fire of the Skysweeper requires an electrically driven loading mechanism, which comprises a rammer to insert the shell and a fuze setter to time the delay before it explodes. The sequence is : 1 the round is pushed from the rammer tray into the slowly rotating ramming rolls. 2 the ramming rolls move the round into the jaws of the fuze setter. When it is securely seated, the rolls stall and the round is held firmly while the jaws revolve, turning the time ring on the shell to set the fuze. 3 the jaws unlock, the rolls shift into high speed and propel the round into the gun chamber. The breechblock closes and the round is fired. 4 the breechblock opens and the spent case is ejected.

signal determines when the fuze should detonate the shell.

Types of AA gun During World War 2 the development of the AA gun reached its peak with two types of weapon—one for defence against low level attack and the other to counter medium and high level sorties.

The light AA (LAA) gun was extremely mobile and capable of very rapid deployment. A high rate of traverse and elevation was essential because at close ranges the angular rate of change of the target was very large. The most popular calibres were 20 mm and 40 mm. The 20 mm guns were used singly, in pairs or on quadruple mountings, and fired fuzed high explosive shells at the rate of 500–700 rounds per minute. These guns were aimed by hand with open 'cartwheel' type sights and engaged targets flying up to 400 mph (640 km/h) at ranges of 1000 yards (900 m) or less. Both sides used similar kinds of guns designed almost entirely by the Swiss firms of Oerlikon and Hispano-Suiza. The 40 mm guns were less mobile than those of 20 mm but the greater high explosive content of their shell ensured that a hit was virtually certain to bring an aircraft down. They generally fired at about 120 rounds a minute at targets up to 500 feet (150 m) and although the great majority used relatively simple open sights, predictors were sometimes used to calculate the future position of the target and aim the gun accurately.

Right: a 40 mm Bofors light anti-aircraft gun, capable of firing up to 120 impact fuzed rounds per minute. It was designed in Sweden, and large numbers of them were produced in Britain during World War 2.

Below: an automatic 40 mm anti-aircraft gun used by the US Navy. It is used on several types of ship, and can fire 160 rounds per minute over a range of 11,000 yards (10,000 metres).

POPPERFOTO

U.S. NAVY

The Heavy AA (HAA) guns varied from 3 inch calibre through 3.7 inch and 4.5 inch up to 5.25 inch and could engage targets up to 60,000 feet (18,300 m). Owing to the great height and speed of the targets the fire control equipment was complicated and the need to fire the largest possible shell made automatic loading mandatory. The high muzzle velocity required to cut down the time of flight, and the rapid rate of fire needed to give the greatest chance of a hit, led to excessive barrel wear and short accuracy life for these guns.

The future of the AA gun The invention of the jet engine gave aircraft the ability to reach greater heights and to fly at higher speeds and the HAA gun is now obsolete. The chance of a hit has so diminished that they have passed out of service in all modern forces and have been replaced by ground to air MISSILES which can change course in flight, fly to great heights and automatically seek out and destroy the target before it can reach the point at which it can release its bomb load.

The increased use of very high speed jet fighter bombers in the battle zone has led to the retention of 20 and 30 mm LAA guns firing at very high rates of fire and often fitted with complex controlling gear frequently linked to early warning and control radars.

Missiles operated by one man, such as the British 'Blowpipe', are being developed to seek out the low level attacking aircraft and may become commonplace although the relative cheapness of the LAA gun and its ammunition may enable it to remain in service for many years to come.

A Blowpipe missile being launched. To protect the user from injury by flame or blast, the first stage burns for only a fraction of a second, the main stage being ignited when the missile is at a safe distance.

ANTIBIOTIC MANUFACTURE

Antibiotics are a useful group of chemical substances produced by certain types of micro-organisms. In low concentrations, they can kill or stop the growth of other micro-organisms which cause diseases in man, in animals and in plants.

True antibiotics are produced by moulds, bacteria, or actinomycetes (organisms intermediate between bacteria and moulds). Others may be chemically synthesized, or modified from the molecule of a naturally occurring antibiotic. Technically, they are then no longer true antibiotics but are just as effective in fighting diseases. Over 2000 antibiotics have been identified or synthesized, and of these, about 60 have been produced commercially.

The majority of the antibiotics are used in human and veterinary medicine as antibacterial agents; others are used to treat fungal infections, such as ringworm, in man and in animals, or fungal diseases affecting crops; some are effective against protozoal infections such as amoebic dysentery; a few are used in the treatment of some rare types of cancer.

Antibiotic research stems from the accidental discovery by Sir Alexander Fleming, in 1928, of a colony of *Penicillium* mould contaminating a laboratory culture of staphylococci, the bacteria causing boils and blood-poisoning. Substances produced by the mould colony had diffused out and killed the surrounding staphylococci. Tests showed that the mould could also kill or inhibit the growth of a number of other kinds of disease causing bacteria, but for several years researchers were unable to isolate the active agent, which was highly unstable. When penicillin was eventually isolated in very small quantities, clinical trials demonstrated its potential medical value, and the advent of World War 2 provided the impetus for large scale commercial development.

Production techniques British manufacturers commenced production using the only available method, which was basically a laboratory technique. The *Penicillium* mould was grown on the surface of a nutrient liquid (see below) in thousands of glass flasks. Once the mould colony had spread to cover the surface of the nutrient, it was filtered off, and the crude penicillin, which had diffused from the mould into the liquid, extracted from the liquid. A very low yield was obtained, and there were additional problems with contamination of the culture by other micro-organisms.

Meanwhile manufacturers in the United States concentrated on improved methods, and perfected the technique of deep fermentation now used for the production of most antibiotics. Deep fermentation was based on the discovery of a species of *Penicillium* which would grow submerged in the nutrient liquid, rather than as a thin skin on the surface, thus producing a higher yield of penicillin from a given volume of liquid. Further strains and artificial mutations of *Penicillium* were produced, with improved yields, and finally, the discovery of a new liquid increased the yield ten-fold.

Above: Professor Alexander Fleming in his laboratory where research into antibiotics began with his discovery of pencillin in 1928.

Below: a pencillin culture flask, dating back 30 years, containing the growing mould. In the final stage, the mould ferments in large tanks.

In modern production, master cultures of selected strains of *Penicillium* are stored in controlled conditions, to ensure uniformity of subsequent production. Small sub-cultures are transferred to culture flasks, allowed to develop on a suitable liquid medium, then transferred to a larger vessel. Once again, the culture develops and is transferred to progressively larger fermenters until it reaches the final stage, where the fermenting tank, which is usually made of stainless steel, may be of 30,000 gallons (136,000 litres) capacity.

The mould grows submerged in a sterilized nutrient broth based on corn-steep liquor (a by-product of the starch manufacturing industry), sugar, salts, and other carefully controlled ingredients which are used to modify the penicillin molecule. The final fermentation is complete after 1 to 2 weeks, when the contents of the tank are drawn off and filtered to remove the *Penicillium* mould. The remaining liquid, containing the penicillin, is chemically purified and concentrated. A final chemical process precipitates penicillin out in a fine crystalline form, which is filtered out, washed with a solvent to remove impurities, dried and stored.

DISTA PRODUCTS

Above: two antibiotic crystallization units in operation with the associated pipe connection panel. First dissolved in preparation tanks, the antibiotics are next sterilized by filtration and then conveyed to the crystallizers through the pipe panel. Before a batch of material is processed, the whole system is sterilized. The pipe panel allows solutions to be fed to either crystallizer from any of several tanks.

Left: this symmetrical colony of green mould is Penicillium chrysogenum. *A mutant form of this mould has become very important because it produces almost all commercial penicillin.*

Each batch is rigorously tested to ensure its activity and purity, and the entire manufacturing process takes place under sterile conditions. By varying the constituents of the nutrient broth, chemically different forms of penicillin can be produced, and the penicillin molecule can be further modified by chemical treatment after purification to produce semi-synthetic penicillins which do not occur in nature. More extensive modifications to the basic molecule can produce entirely new antibiotics, such as ampicillin and cephalexin. Other types of antibiotic are manufactured using similar fermentation processes.

Antibiotic applications

Penicillin and related antibiotics are extremely active against many different types of bacteria; other antibiotics have activity against more restricted groups of micro-organisms. Broad-spectrum antibiotics such as the tetracyclines and chloramphenicol, which is used for typhoid, can also be used for a wide variety of bacterial infections, and a similar effect is sometimes obtained by combining antibiotics with narrower ranges of activity.

Allergic reactions and side effects of varying severity may be experienced in a proportion of patients treated with antibiotics. In addition, antibiotic-resistant strains of bacteria have emerged, and diseases which formerly responded rapidly to antibiotic treatment sometimes cause problems, particularly in hospitals. For these reasons, the antibiotic activity of a wide range of micro-organisms is continuously monitored, in an attempt to discover broad-spectrum antibiotics with a minimum of undesirable side effects, and which will hopefully prevent the emergence of resistant strains.

One result of such a screening programme was cephaloridine, derived from an antibiotic produced by *Cephalosporium*, a mould collected from the Mediterranean in 1945. In laboratory studies, 40,000 mutated strains of the mould were tested until one was selected, yielding sufficient quantities of the natural antibiotic substance, which was then chemically modified to produce cephaloridine. Further modification to the cephaloridine molecule produced cephalixin, which can also be prepared by modifying the penicillin molecule.

In addition to the above activities, some antibiotics have a marked growth promoting effect on livestock, and are often incorporated in small amounts into animal feeds for this purpose. Because of fears that antibiotic-resistant strains of bacteria might develop in treated livestock, and subsequently be transferred to humans, only a limited range of these antibiotics, none of which are used in human medicine, is permitted in animal feeds in many countries.

In Japan and the USA, much research has been carried out on antibiotics for horticultural purposes, mainly to combat fungal diseases of crops, such as rusts and smuts. Large scale production allows 10,000 tons of blasticidin-S to be used annually in Japan as a treatment for Rice Blast, a serious fungal disease of rice paddies.

Below: the final stage in the antibiotic crystallization process. The crystals are washed with a solvent mixture and then directed to a lower level where they are dried in a vacuum. The man standing is checking the flow of the mixture, while the other man is taking a sample of the waste to make certain there is no loss of antibiotic.

ANTI-FOULING TECHNIQUES

Anti-fouling techniques are used to keep ships' hulls and other objects which are submerged in the sea, such as buoys and oil rigs, free from animals and vegetation. Unchecked infestation will severely decrease the speed of a ship and will require additional fuel to overcome the drop in performance. To this must be added the cost of docking, loss of earnings and the financial burden of carrying out remedial measures.

The organisms which settle on ships' hulls disturb the smooth flow of water and cause an increase in drag which turns out in practice to be about 0.25% per day for temperate waters. After six months, a ship's top speed may be cut by up to 2 knots, and about 40% more fuel is used in keeping up cruising speed.

The most common fouling species are barnacles and green algae, but in some regions tube-worms, hydroids, sea-squirts, mussels, and various red and brown algae also give trouble. Even when killed, barnacles cause an increase in drag by the presence of their empty shells.

Anti-fouling paints are still the most efficient means of achieving protection. They contain toxicants, chemicals that are poisonous to fouling organisms. Cuprous oxide is the most universally used but it is often 'boosted' with other compounds such as tributyltin oxide. In order to be effective, the toxicants have to dissolve out of the paint into the surrounding water.

Types of coating

There are two types of anti-fouling paint, the first in which the matrix (base material) is insoluble and the second in which it is slightly soluble. Included in the former are materials such as vinyls, and in the latter the acidic resin known as rosin.

Soluble matrix coating, being slightly acidic, react with the seawater. This releases the toxicant slowly. With paints of the insoluble kind new layers of cuprous oxide particles are exposed to the seawater as the outer ones dissolve, while the matrix itself remains in place. In addition there are coatings which rely on mechanical erosion, produced by the water flow over the surface, to expose the toxicant which then dissolves in the water.

Ancient practice

The fouling problem is a very ancient one and probably dates from the time that man first ventured, in his primitive craft, upon the waters of this planet. As early as 200 BC the Greek writer Atheneus records that the ships of Archimedes were fastened with copper bolts and the entire bottom sheathed with lead. This first consideration, in those days, was to prevent the wood-destroying 'ship-worm' and 'gribble' from attacking the timbers, although the benefits of controlling fouling were realized.

In the 4th and 5th centuries the Phoenicians, Carthaginians and Greeks used a variety of methods which included coatings of pitch, wax and a mixture of arsenic, sulphur and oil. Such practices were continued for centuries, but provided only short-term protection.

Below : the effects of anti-fouling on steel. The section on the right was not treated for fouling, allowing barnacles and algae to collect. The red of the middle section comes from the cuprous oxide used in anti-fouling paint, while the section on the left shows only a mud slime.

The Phoenicians are also said to have employed copper sheathing, but it was not until the 18th century that this material was widely used. The first authenticated case was that of the Royal Naval vessel, HMS *Alarm*, in 1758. The absence of fouling was noted but the cause remained a mystery. It was not until 1824, as a result of the researches of Sir Humphry DAVY, that the toxic effects of dissolved copper were recognized.

The disadvantages of using copper sheathing were that it was expensive and it dissolved comparatively rapidly, causing the iron nails used in the construction of the ship and the rudder irons to corrode.

With the evolution of iron and steel hulled ships, the electrolytic reaction between copper and the metal of the hull, resulting in corrosion, made the use of such sheathing totally impractical. It was then that the scientists turned their attention to developing anti-fouling coatings.

Traditionally, it was considered that the average time between dry-dockings for defouling was six to nine months. Present day anti-fouling paints can give protection for two and a half to three years.

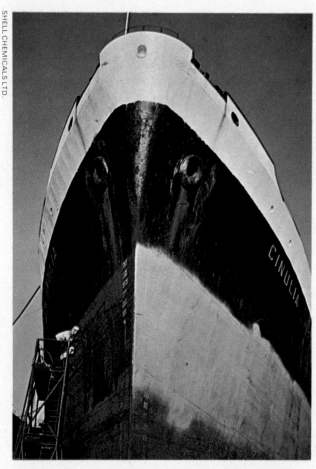

SHELL CHEMICALS LTD.

Above: the hull of the tanker 'Cinulia', which has been treated with anti-fouling paints. A badly fouled vessel suffers a serious reduction in speed and requires a substantial increase in fuel consumption to maintain a given speed. Fundamental properties required for effective anti-fouling paint are that it should have good adhesion and present a smooth surface, as well as preventing fouling by the controlled release of the toxic constituents which check potential infestation.

It has been calculated that the war against Japan was shortened by as much as 18 months because Japanese anti-fouling techniques lagged behind those of the United States. The enemy ships had to return to port for defouling every nine months and it was expected that American ships would have to do the same. On several occasions the Japanese attacked targets expecting US guard ships to be safely in dry dock when in fact they were not, and as a consequence the attacker sustained heavy losses.

At present, attention is being paid to developing improved anti-fouling paints, more effective toxicants, alternative methods of distributing these compounds, and methods which do not require the use of toxicants at all. In the latter case, research is trying to find compounds, both synthetic and naturally occurring, which make it impossible for the organisms to attach themselves to the craft, without actually killing them.

ANTIMATTER (see atom; particle physics; vacuum;

AQUALUNG

The aqualung [or SCUBA, short for self contained underwater breathing apparatus] is a system which allows a diver to carry his air supply with him when he dives. He is thus freed of any direct links with the surface and has much greater flexibility of movement than the 'helmet' diver, who needs air and safety lines.

The aqualung diver's stay under water is limited by the capacity of the air cylinders he carries. Nevertheless, the dive times afforded by the aqualung have made it an important tool in underwater science and technology, and in search and rescue operations, while it has opened the way for diving as a sport throughout the world.

The aqualung consists of five basic components: a demand valve or regulator, which reduces the high pressure air supply to ambient pressures (the same pressure as the water around the diver); the cylinders, which contain compressed air; the harness which keeps the apparatus in the correct position relative to the diver's body; the tubes for air delivery and exhaust; and the mouthpiece through which he sucks the air. All are vital, but it is the demand valve which is the most complex and ingenious.

The human body has evolved on dry land and therefore is designed to withstand the kind of pressures exerted on it by the air (one atmosphere or 14.7 psi at sea level). Water, though, is much more dense than air, and the diver's body is subjected to much greater pressure in water than on land. The deeper he goes, the stronger these pressures become. Seawater exerts a pressure of two atmospheres at 33 feet (10 m), and this increases by one atmosphere for every additional 33 feet (10 m) of depth.

The body consists largely of solids and liquids that are virtually incompressible, even under very great pressures. But it also contains cavities which are filled with air—the lungs, the sinuses, the inner ear, and the stomach—all of which connect with the respiratory system. Thus, if the air breathed in is not at the same pressure as the water around the body, these cavities will be forced to contract. As air is easily compressed, breathing will become extremely hard work even at relatively shallow depths, and if the diver goes deep enough, the pressure will crush the cavities flat and kill him.

Demand valve The job of the demand valve is to see that these problems do not occur. The simplest form is a circular box connected on one side to the outlet of the high pressure cylinder. The other side is open to allow seawater to enter, but the water does not flood the box—it is stopped by a rubber diaphragm inside the open face. The diaphragm is connected within the box to a valve controlling the air supply from the cylinder, and when the diaphragm is pressed inwards that valve is opened.

The external pressure, whether atmospheric or that of the sea, pushes the diaphragm in. This opens the air valve until just enough air has been let in on the cylinder side to balance the pressure. The pressures on both sides of the valve are then equal, so the air the diver breathes must be at ambient pressure.

When the diver breathes this air, he creates a partial vacuum inside the air chamber. The outside pressure opens the valve again, and the process continues.

This single stage design has the disadvantage that the high pressures to be controlled by the valve put a heavy strain on it. A modification to overcome this is the two stage type, in which the first stage brings the air down from around 3000 psi (200 bar) to about 100 psi (7 bar) above ambient pressure by means of a valve acting against pre-set spring pressure. The air can then be brought to ambient pressure by a device similar to the single stage type.

In the split-stage or single hose type, the first stage is mounted on the cylinder itself, which is connected by a single small-diameter pressure hose to the face mask, where the second demand valve stage is located.

Some demand valves have inlets where air lines can be fitted to supply air at fairly low pressure from cylinders or a COM-PRESSOR at the surface. This allows the diver to stay submerged for a long time.

Cylinders and harness
The cylinders which carry the air supply are relatively simple. They are made in various sizes, and the divers like them to be buoyant when empty so that they will float to the surface after use. They are painted grey with black and white quarters at the top, a conventional code to show which gas they contain—in this case air. A typical cylinder might contain about 60 cu ft (1.7 m³) of air compressed at a pressure of around 3000 psi (200 bar).

The deeper the diver goes, the more air he uses for each intake of breath. Thus the depth of a dive has a bearing on its length in time. Cylinders which contain enough air for an hour's diving at 33 feet (10 m) will only support the diver for 30 minutes at 100 feet (30 m). Other variations in the time scale arise because the diver needs more air the harder he works, or when he is cold.

The harness is usually of nylon or cotton webbing with steel bands. Its task is not only to hold the cylinders in place on the diver's back, but also to make sure that the demand valve is as near the centre of ambient pressure in his lungs as possible.

Development
The first really dependable aqualung system was developed by Jaques-Yves Cousteau and Emil Gagnan, but their work was preceded and undoubtedly helped by many other attempts at providing the diver with a truly self contained breathing system. Much of this was at first concerned with mine rescue work. As early as 1879, a British designer named H A Fleuss demonstrated a diving set in London in which air was carried in a flexible bag on his back. The diver breathed used air back into the bag, but on the way carbon dioxide was removed from it by caustic potash.

Since only a small percentage of the oxygen is used in each intake of air, a relatively small reservoir of air could last a long time. The oxygen actually used was replenished from a small cylinder which he also carried, and this allowed him to stay underwater even longer.

The device was only suitable for shallow depths and even then must have made breathing hard work for it had no demand valve. But it was good enough to enable Fleuss to clear obstructions from a tunnel under the River Severn which flooded in 1880.

Other attempts to devise effective self contained gear took place right up to the outbreak of World War 2, but they all —American, German and British—contained some basic flaw.

It was left to Cousteau and his colleague, working in German occupied France to solve the problems—in particular to produce the demand valve which has given the diver greater freedom underwater.

Top: a design for a self-contained diving suit by Vannoccio Biringuccio, published in his 'Pirotechnia' of 1540.

Above: a modern naval 'frogman' wearing an aqualung with two cylinders of compressed air. The rubber suit helps to protect the frogman when diving in cold waters.

ERIC JEWELL ASSOC.

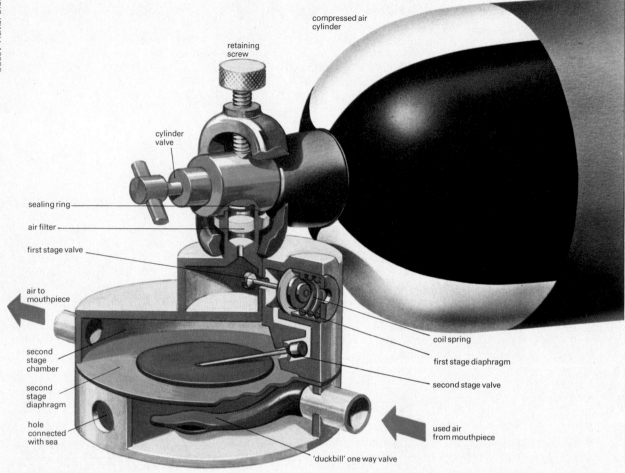

compressed air
cylinder

retaining
screw

cylinder
valve

sealing ring

air filter

first stage valve

air to
mouthpiece

coil spring

first stage diaphragm

second
stage
chamber

second stage valve

second
stage
diaphragm

hole
connected
with sea

used air
from mouthpiece

'duckbill' one way valve

Above : section through a typical two stage demand valve. The high pressure of the air in the cylinder is reduced in two stages to the level of the surrounding water by two sets of valves and chambers. In each set the valve is opened by the pressure 'downstream' of it falling below a certain level. The high pressure of the first stage, which would normally hold the valve shut, is balanced by a coil spring.

Below : three stages in the working of the valve. Air at higher pressure than the water is shown in red, at roughly the same pressure in orange and at lower pressure in yellow. The diver opens the second stage valve by inhaling and so lowering the pressure in the second stage chamber. The first stage refills itself automatically when emptied. Exhaled air is released nearby to equalize its pressure with the incoming air.

ERIC JEWELL ASSOC.

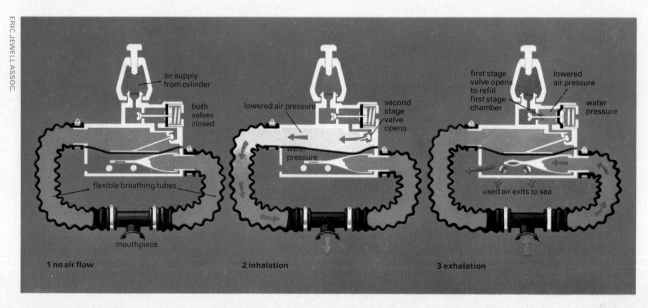

air supply
from cylinder

both
valves
closed

flexible breathing tubes

mouthpiece

1 no air flow

lowered air pressure

second
stage
valve opens

water
pressure

2 inhalation

first stage
valve opens
to refill
first stage
chamber

lowered
air pressure

water
pressure

used air exits to sea

3 exhalation

ARCHAEOLOGICAL TECHNIQUES

Archaeology is undergoing a scientific revolution. Traditionally the procedures of archaeology have involved excavating sites, uncovering artifacts, the products of human workmanship, and establishing a chronology or time scale against which the artifacts can be dated. These procedures are still vital, but they are being supplemented by techniques and instruments drawn from a wide range of sciences.

A firm chronology can be provided by scientific dating methods. By analyzing the composition of artifacts, the sources of their raw materials are often revealed—essential in understanding ancient trade and technology. Zoology and botany are used to give insights into the environment of our ancestors, and to show how they utilized the plants and animals of their time. The excavation process itself is being speeded by scientific methods for locating sites on the ground, by developments in photographic recording and by computerized data storage.

Discovery of sites AERIAL PHOTOGRAPHY has revealed many new archaeological sites. An earthwork, ploughed so that it is difficult to recognize at ground level, can be seen from the air when the sun is at a very low angle and the slight ridges and hollows are clearly revealed by their long shadows. Some sites are totally invisible from the ground but, under suitable conditions of climate and crop, may be seen from the air by means of *crop marks*. Buried pits and ditches filled with good topsoil will retain moisture so that the vegetation above them will grow taller and greener, while buried roads and walls provide a well drained infertile subsoil stunting crop growth. When ploughing cuts into archaeological features such as ditches of walls, the topsoil may become coloured with

materials brought up from these, so that the site shows as a *soil mark*.

Before excavation, it is necessary to pinpoint archaeological features on the ground and a number of instruments have been specially developed for this purpose. Resistivity meters are used to measure the RESISTANCE of the soil to the passage of an electric current. Electricity is conducted by water in the ground containing dissolved mineral salts, and hence well drained soils will have a greater resistance than less drained ones. Since buried archaeological features will retain moisture to differing degrees they can be detected by their contrasting electrical resistance. In carrying out a resistivity survey, four equally spaced iron rods are inserted into the ground in a straight line, and an alternating electric current is passed through the outer two while the resistance is assessed on a meter connected to the inner pair. The rods are moved across the field in a series of parallel traverses to record variations. An alternative scheme, which greatly speeds survey, has the meter mounted on a table with four sharp iron probes as legs: current is passed through one pair and the resistance assessed across the other.

The proton MAGNETOMETER has been developed to measure minute variations in magnetism and surveys of this type can be a rapid way of detecting archaeological features on sites which are not magnetically disturbed by electric pylons or the underlying bedrock. Most soils and rocks contain a scatter of minute iron oxide particles, each of which has a weak magnetic field. These fields are randomly orientated and tend to cancel one another out. If the raw material in which they are embedded is heated above about 700° C (1300° F), the particles lose their magnetism and on cooling they will all

The chalk uplands of southern England have been more intensively studied from the air from an archaeological point of view than any other. These photographs show a farm at Little Wittenham, Berkshire, in an area which has many signs of Iron Age occupation, dating from about 1000 BC. The camera used took both pictures simultaneously, the one on the left being on ordinary colour film, that on the right an

infra-red false colour film. Vague markings, quite invisible from the ground, are seen in the field near the barn. These are clarified by the false colour picture, where they are outlined in red and blue. The markings are caused by ditches long since filled in, but more fertile than the parched background: they reflect infra-red light better. A dry summer is good for spotting crop marks.

Left : a square array resistivity system. Current passed through the legs on one side spreads through the soil around them : the voltage produced can then be measured across the other pair. A computer produces a map of the area (below), the number of dots varying with the reading. This map shows a site where gas pipe laying uncovered walls where no building was known to have been : surveys revealed a Roman villa.

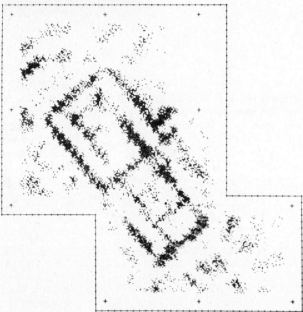

re-magnetize in the direction of the earth's field. The particles will now reinforce one another so that the magnetic field of the material will be greatly increased. For this reason, kilns and hearths where the ground has been heated can be readily detected by their relatively strong magnetic effect. Pits and ditches filled with topsoil also have a slightly enhanced magnetic field because the iron oxide particles align themselves with the earth's field to a slight degree even without heating, and because burning associated with human occupation tends to alter iron oxide to the more magnetic varieties.

METAL DETECTORS are of considerably less value in archaeology than is commonly believed. If an excavation is properly conducted, metal artifacts will be recovered in the normal course and it can be positively damaging to dig small holes, removing them from their proper archaeological context.

Dating methods

The invention of *radiocarbon* dating has had a profound effect on archaeological chronologies. Small quantities of the radioactive ISOTOPE carbon 14 are formed in the upper atmosphere when the nirtogen in the air is bombarded with cosmic rays. The newly formed isotope, contained in the gas carbon dioxide, is distributed throughuot the earth's atmosphere, taken up by plants and passed to the animal kingdom in food. All living matter contains minute quantities of carbon 14 constantly supplied from the 'reservoir' in the upper atmosphere. On death the supply is not renewed and the quantity of carbon 14 gradually diminishes at a constant rate as the unstable isotope decays back to nitrogen. Thus the amount of carbon 14 present in a sample of wood or bone will relate to its age.

Since isotopes are chemically identical with their related atoms it is difficult to actually isolate carbon 14, but the

Below : excavation has to be carefully controlled and detailed records made, so that when an object is unearthed, its relative position below ground, and hence its chronology, is established. The preliminary to this is often a mapping survey, particularly where there are few existing reference points. A grid of posts and strings is then set up.

amount present can be estimated by measuring the radio-activity of the sample. This is usually done by converting the material to a gas such as methane (CH_4) and measuring its RADIOACTIVITY with a sensitive GEIGER COUNTER shielded from atmospheric radiation by a thick armour of lead. Another way is to convert the sample to the liquid benzene (C_6H_6) and measure with a scintillation counter, another kind of PARTICLE DETECTOR. The date can be calculated with knowledge of the present day radioactivity of the sample, the radioactivity it would originally have had and the decay rate (half life) of carbon 14.

In the early development of the method, the original radio-activity was estimated by assuming that the amount of carbon 14 in the atmosphere and hence in living matter had remained constant over the past few thousand years, but this has recently been shown to be untrue by taking measurements of carbon 14 in trees. Trees grow by adding a fresh ring of wood to their circumference annually: in a good growth year the ring will be a broad one, in a bad year a narrow one. Tree rings are easily visible in almost any log of wood and if the life spans of two trees overlap it should be possible to see parts of the same thick and thin ring pattern appear in each. By cross dating in this way it is sometimes possible to establish a long sequence of wood samples and if the date of any one tree ring is known it is possible to date all the rings in the sequence. In America a tree ring series has been built up for the past 7000 years, using the long-lived bristlecone pine tree, and study of the carbon 14 content of individual dated rings has shown that there must have been significant variations in the carbon 14 content of the earth's atmosphere—enough to cause serious errors in the calculated date. For example, the early radio-carbon dates for the beginning of farming in northwestern Europe centred around 3000 BC, but the bristlecone pine work suggests that they are about 500 years too young.

Tree ring dating, or *dendrochronology*, is a valuable technique in its own right. It has been extensively used, for example, in the excavations on the mediaeval Russian town of Novgorod, where damp conditions were responsible for the preservation of a remarkable sequence of timber streets and buildings. Comparison of ring widths in numerous wood samples established a tree ring sequence which spanned the whole period of the mediaeval town and absolute dates were given by wood samples from beams in standing churches of known foundation date. The last ring in these beams would date to the season immediately preceding the foundation year, so the ring sequence was tied and every log of wood from Novgorod could be dated to the very year in which it was felled.

Thermoluminescent dating, first demonstrated at Oxford in 1968, is proving valuable in assessing the age of fired materials such as pottery. Radioactive particles given off by the decay of the isotopes found in any crystalline substance tend to 'knock off' electrons from the atoms of which it is made. Some of these become trapped in imperfections in the crystal structure and these trapped electrons accumulate with the passage of time.

When the crystalline matter is heated, the electrons are released and energy is given off in the form of light. The intensity of the glow is related to the age of the crystal or to the time that has elapsed since the material was heated by early man, since this drives off the geologically accumulated glow and the build up begins again. Particles of quartz are present in almost all ceramics, and these crystals are commonly used in dating. Thermoluminescence has proved of great value in the fine art world as it is a rapid and almost infallible way of distinguishing ancient ceramics from modern forgeries.

Artifact analysis Microscopes are often used in studying the composition of artifacts. By examining thin transparent slices of stone implements, the rock from which they are made can be determined. Comparing the details of mineralogy and texture with samples from present day rocks often makes it possible to find out precisely where the original rock came from. In Britain, a long programme of research on

Above: part of a radiocarbon dating apparatus. The vertical cylinder on the right is a 'combustion bomb' in which the sample to be dated is vaporized. Carbon dioxide given off is carried along a glass tube to the apparatus on the left to be turned first into acetylene, then into liquid benzene. Its radioactivity is measured in this form.

Left: marine archaeology is becoming increasingly important as a means of discovering structures of ancient ships and the cargoes they carried. These are the ribs of a pre-Roman ship found off Sicily.

late Stone Age axes has demonstrated remarkable country-wide transportation at this early period. Rock and mineral inclusions in pottery can be examined in the same way: interesting results have been obtained in both western Britain and in New Mexico, where certain groups of prehistoric pottery, previously assumed to be of local manufacture, were clearly traded over considerable distances. The microscopic examination of metal artifacts does not provide information about origin, but the form and relationship of metal crystals helps in understanding the technology of metal working.

Chemical analysis of artifacts is usually done by optical emission SPECTROSCOPY. A small sample is burnt between carbon rods carrying an electric current, the light is split by prisms and the resulting spectrum photographed. The position of dark lines on the photographic plate will indicate what chemical elements are present and in what quantities. This has made it possible to distinguish groups of artifacts with similar compositions, and hence, probably, similar origins.

Outstanding success has been achieved with obsidian, a natural volcanic glass, used in many parts of the world for the manufacture of sharp stone implements. Obsidian occurs in only a few locations and research in the eastern Mediterranean has shown that each outcrop has its own characteristic content of minor elements. Finds from archaeological sites can be assigned to their parent outcrop after analysis and a picture emerges showing when different sources were exploited and how the products were traded over many hundreds of miles.

Optical emission spectroscopy is now being replaced to an increasing extent by *neutron activation analysis*, which can be non-destructive and more accurate. A small sample is subjected to a flow of neutrons in an atomic reactor, converting many of the elements present to their radioactive isotopes. These decay, producing a characteristic radiation, and by analysing the gamma rays given off it is possible to assess accurately many of the elements present. The method will provide information about rare trace elements difficult to detect by other means and these are proving useful in characterizing materials such as pottery or obsidian.

Environment The study of biological remains from archaeological sites does not usually require elaborate equipment. A sample of soil may be agitated in water using a flotation machine, in which small seeds, charcoal fragments, bones, snails and insect remains will float to the surface. These can give information about diet, vegetation and sometimes climate.

Pollen is extremely resistant and is often well preserved in lake muds, heathland soils and particularly in peat bogs. These are important as they contain a pollen record of vegetational, and hence climate, changes that have taken place in the region while the bog was forming. Pollen is extracted by destroying other organic and mineral matter with strong acids: this drastic treatment does not affect the pollen which can be collected as a residue and examined under a microscope.

Soils can also indicate something of past climate and vegetational cover, as characteristic types form in different environments. The main features are studied in the field, additional information being obtained in the laboratory, from study of grain-size, texture, chemistry and mineralogy.

Above: when a pot is fired in a kiln, magnetic particles in it will align themselves with the Earth's magnetic field, the direction of which changes with time. The pot is being spun inside the coils of a magnetometer: the current produced in the coils enables the original field direction to be determined. If the orientation of the pot in the kiln is known, its date can be found—in this case about 500 AD.

Above: thin slices of ceramic or rock are ground on a diamond milling lap, shown here. The process continues until the slice is about 0.03 mm (1 thou) thick, and almost transparent. It can then be examined under a microscope, or a photomicrograph taken (left). This one shows a section of an Iron Age pot from Sutton Walls hill fort, Herefordshire. In it can be seen fragments of limestone, probably from the Malvern area. At the centre is a concretion of fossilized algae.